SCIENCE
COURSE BOOK

Kathryn Sharp, Michael McComiskie
and Graeme McKellan

First published in 2019 by:
Bright Red Publishing Ltd
1 Torphichen Street
Edinburgh
EH3 8HX

The rights of Kathryn Sharp, Graeme McKellan and Michael McComiskie to be identified as the authors of this work have been asserted by them in accordance with Sections 77 and 78 of the Copyright, Designs and Patents Act 1988.

A CIP record for this book is available from the British Library.

ISBN 978-1-84948-314-8

With thanks to: PDQ Digital Media Solutions Ltd, Bungay (layout), Anna Clark (copy-edit).

Cover design and series book design by Caleb Rutherford – e i d e t i c.

Acknowledgements

We were very lucky that our boss, Steve Hoffman, shared our vision and supported us wholly in the very drastic change to themed, skills-based topics that merged the different sciences within a narrative of experiences and outcomes. Our department of Denny High School embraced the course and we have been teaching this themed approach to science successfully for the last few years. This book has come out of our course development, born from a desire to excite pupils and help fellow teachers in their work.

This one's for you Steve.

Every effort has been made to seek all copyright-holders. If any have been overlooked, then Bright Red Publishing will be delighted to make the necessary arrangements.

Permission has been sought from all relevant copyright holders and Bright Red Publishing are grateful for the use of the following:

Images licensed by Ingram Images (pp 8–9, 34, 44, 55, 56, 59, 60, 61, 74, 77, 78, 105, 106, 111, 114, 115, 119, 121, 125, 128, 129, 135, 138, 139, 167, 173, 176, 180, 187 & 190); Caleb Rutherford – e i d e t i c (pp 36–7); Courtesy NASA/JPL-Caltech (p 38); Caleb Rutherford – e i d e t i c (pp 39 & 40); zeitfaenger.at/Creative Commons (CC BY 2.0)[1] (p 41); Courtesy NASA/JPL-Caltech (p 41); Caleb Rutherford – e i d e t i c (p 42); NASA, ESA, and the Hubble Heritage Team (STScI/AURA)-ESA/Hubble Collaboration (p 50); Kelvinsong/Creative Commins (CC BY-SA 3.0)[2] (p 52); Courtesy NASA/JPL-Caltech (p 52); Quote reproduced with permission of Intergovernmental Panel on Climate Change (p 54); Quote reproduced with permission of National Academy of Sciences (p 54); Rhododendrites/Creative Commons (CC BY-SA 4.0)[3] (p 55); Nick Bramhall/Creative Commons (CC BY-SA 2.0)[4] (p 55); Four images by James St. John/Creative Commons (CC BY 2.0)[1] (pp 56–57); The Portable Antiquities Scheme/Creative Commons (CC BY-SA 2.0)[4] (p 60); Blueshade/Creative Commons (CC BY-SA 2.0)[4] (p 64); Tau'olunga (CC BY-SA 3.0)[2] (p 65); ktsimage/iStock.com (p 67); claudiodivizia/iStock.com (p 67); Courtesy NASA/JPL-Caltech (p 68); Courtesy NASA/JPL-Caltech/University of Nantes/University of Arizona (p 71); Courtesy NASA/JPL-Caltech (p 71); Geology In (pp 73 & 90); ABelov2014/Creative Commons (CC BY-SA 3.0)[2] (p 74); Mnolf/Creative Commons (CC BY-SA 3.0)[2] (p 77); Yohan euan o4/Creative Commons (CC BY-SA 3.0)[2] (p 77); H. Zell/Creative Commons (CC BY-SA 3.0)[2] (p 81); http://www.kvins.com/Creative Commons (CC BY 2.0)[1] (p 81); SuSanA Secretariat/Creative Commons (CC BY 2.0)[1] (p 81); Barnesy Barnes (CC BY-SA 3.0)[2] (p 86); PRZ/Creative Commons (CC BY-SA 3.0)[2] (p 86); Cunningchrisw/Creative Commons (CC BY-SA 4.0)[3] (p 87); Image by the NASA Global Climate Change website. Data: Luthi, D., et al. 2008. Etheridge, D.M., et al. 2010. Vostok ice core data/J.R. Petit et al. NOAA Mauna Loa CO2 record (p 87); Walter Baxter/Creative Commons (CC BY-SA 2.0)[4] (p 88); ZooFari/Creative Commons (CC BY-SA 3.0)[2] (p 99); www.createhealth.com (CC BY 2.0)[1] (p 101); Thinkpaul/Creative Commons (CC BY-SA 3.0)[2] (p 101); Bildagentur Zoonar GmbH/Shutterstock.com (p 106); OpenStaz College/Creative Commons (CC BY-SA 3.0)[2] (p 106); Iceclanl/Creative Commons (CC BY-SA 3.0)[2] (p 108); Two images by Nephron/Creative Commons (CC BY-SA 3.0)[2] (p 108); Two images by Ed Uthman/Creative Commons (CC BY 2.0)[1] (p 109); Sebastian Kaulitzki/Shutterstock.com (p 109); Designua/Shutterstock.com (p 109); 'The eatwell guide' taken from: https://www.nhs.uk/Livewell/Goodfood/Documents/The-Eatwell-Guide-2016.pdf © Crown copyright. Contains public sector information licensed under the Open Government Licence v3.0. (http://www.nationalarchives.gov.uk/doc/open-government-licence/version/3/) (p 111); GagliardiPhotography/Shutterstock.com (p 113); BlueRingMedia/Shutterstock.com (p 116); Bruce Blaus/Creative Commons (CC BY-SA 3.0)[2] (p 116); Fernando Frazão/Agência Brasil/Creative Commons (CC BY 3.0 br)[5] (p 122); Peter G. Werner/Creative Commons (CC BY 3.0)[6] (p 124); yangna/iStock.com (p 127); David Stewart/Creative Commons (CC BY 2.0)[1] (p 127); Image reproduced with permission of Chenango Valley Central School (p 132); Wapcaplet, Yaddah, Rhcastilhos, László Németh/Creative Commons (CC BY-SA 3.0)[2] (p 142); Hardwarehank/Creative Commons (CC BY-SA 2.0)[4] (p 148); TripleQuest/Creative Commons (CC BY-SA 3.0)[2] (p 150); Trexer (CC BY-SA 3.0)[2] (p 150); Image © European Nuclear Society (p 159); Tony Mach/Creative Commons (CC BY-SA 3.0)[2] (p 159); Tavoromann/Creative Commons (CC BY-SA 3.0)[2] (p 159); Dnn87/Creative Commons (CC BY-SA 3.0)[2] (p 160); W. Oelen/Creative Commons (CC BY-SA 3.0)[2] (p 160); National Institute of Korean Language/Creative Commons (CC BY-SA 2.5) (p 160); U.S. Geological survey (CC BY 2.0)[1] (p 160); me/Creative Commons (CC BY-SA 2.5) (p 160); Image from https://www.lookwerelearning.com/heat-conduction-experiment/ is reproduced by permission of Selena Robinson (p 165); Sergey Merkulov/Shutterstock (p 165, 214); Marco Verch/Creative Commons (CC BY 2.0)[1] (p 167, 180); Dave Bryant/Creative Commons (CC BY-SA 3.0)[2] (pp 167, 180); Image copyright of The Scotsman Publications and is being used for this purpose with their kind permission (p 170); Brian Stansberry/creative Commons (CC BY 3.0)[6] (p 172); TrickyH/Creative Commons (CC BY-SA 4.0)[3] (p 174); Lucky Linda/Creative Commons (CC BY 2.0)[1] (p 185); I, Luca Galuzzi/Creative Commons (CC BY-SA 2.5) (p 185); PRHaney/Creative Commons (CC BY-SA 3.0)[2] (p 189); leonello/Shutterstock.com (p 193); České Radiokomunikace/Creative Commons (CC BY-SA 3.0 cz)[7] (p 194); Anita van den Broek/Shutterstock.com (p 195); Image is courtesy of: NASA/SDO/AIA (p 195); Nevit Dilmen/Creative Commons (CC BY-SA 3.0)[2] (p 195).

[1] (CC BY 2.0) http://creativecommons.org/licenses/by/2.0/

[2] (CC BY-SA 3.0) http://creativecommons.org/licenses/by-sa/3.0/

[3] (CC BY-SA 4.0) http://creativecommons.org/licenses/by-sa/4.0/

[4] (CC BY-SA 2.0) http://creativecommons.org/licenses/by-sa/2.0/

[5] (CC BY 3.0 br) http://creativecommons.org/licenses/by/3.0/br/

[6] (CC BY 3.0) http://creativecommons.org/licenses/by/3.0/

[7] (CC BY-SA 3.0 cz) http://creativecommons.org/licenses/by-sa/3.0/cz/

Printed and bound by Replika Press Pvt. Ltd.

CONTENTS

INTRODUCTION

When developing the Broad General Education (BGE) curriculum at Denny High School, we hit on a couple of things that gave us pause for thought. The first was the lack of available resources we could use to focus our course development and the second was the fact that knowledge-based science education was becoming much more difficult to teach given what is expected of pupils by the time they finish their BGE. These factors led us to the conclusion that we needed a way to engage the pupils that would allow us to teach them skills as well as knowledge. We aimed to promote the skills that would allow pupils to discover the knowledge for themselves and to excite them by the content of the curriculum by threading a story through the text.

Skill, Skills, Skills...

This book consists of themed, skills-based topics that merge the different sciences within a narrative of experiences and outcomes. It is a resource that can be used in different ways, in class or at home. Your teacher might follow an entire theme, or dip in and out, or use the book to assign homework tasks.

By using this book, working closely with your teacher and regularly practicing your skills you should find that learning science can be an interesting and fun endeavour! The first chapter starts to introduce you to the different skills you will need to be successful at Level 3 science, and that will form the basis of your science education all the way through to Advanced Higher if you choose to go that far.

As we feel that skills development is a major part of scientific learning, we have based the three content chapters around skills-based activities such as:

Classroom Challenges

These can be found throughout the entire book. They are skills-based challenges that help to illustrate the content point they are trying to teach. Each one is different and overall they contain all the different skills; investigative, research and problem solving. Used in conjunction with the content they could be used as lesson ideas, cover work or as an opportunity to check understanding. The answers are included at the back of the book for ease of use too!

Homework Helpers

There are additional skills-based work sheets available online that can be used as homework or in class activities. There is a homework helper for every benchmark to ensure that you have support through the entire curriculum with a skills focus.

How Does That Work

These sections are highlighted to explain complementary science. This feature has been used to ensure that this book is allowing you the opportunity to learn both breadth and depth within your science offering.

Did You Know?

We couldn't help ourselves; sometimes there are fun facts that we felt were too interesting not to share!

End of Chapter Questions

We have made sure to include a comprehensive end of chapter section full of questions related to the content covered in each chapter. These questions can be answered by using the book to look back through, plus the answers are all included at the back!

Using this book

Basing a curriculum around the 'story' and having themes rooted in skills development has helped our department to increase the number of pupils taking science further up the school, it is building our pupils' confidence, helping to address the gender gaps and encouraging pupils into STEM career paths. Whether your teacher builds your course around it, uses it for inspiration or simply as a cover aid, or if you are using it at home to study and revise, we hope that this book can help you start on your journey into STEM. Enjoy!

AN OVERVIEW OF THE BOOK

As you make your way through each chapter, you will come across extracts telling you a story, such as the ones you can see below. Each chapter follows a different narrative to explore new topics, and everything you learn will be linked together by the story – the extracts will help you follow along, so keep an eye out for them as you read on!

Impact!

An asteroid was hurtling through our Solar System at a devastating speed. It came from deep space and was caught in the Sun's gravitational pull. We will learn all about the journey it made through the different objects in the night sky so we build an understanding of our Solar System, considering also if there could be life beyond our reach. We will learn about the impact the asteroid had when it eventually hit the Earth and caused an extinction event so large it changed the entire course of evolution. We will also learn about the ways in which living things on our planet depend on each other and exist together. We will learn about how we can compare the different species and how all living things survive.

During this chapter we will cover the following Benchmarks:

- SCN 3.06a
- SCN 3.08a
- SCN 3.01a
- SCN 3.02a
- SCN 3.03a
- SCN 3.05b
- SCN 3.17a
- SCN 3.17b

Athlete!

Every second counts in the final race of the Triathlon calendar. Every breath and footstep could make the difference between winning and losing. As we follow our athlete through her final race, we will look at how her body works. We will learn to identify some of the organs in her body and understand what vital jobs they do to keep her moving at her fastest pace. We will look deeper into her body systems and learn about the structure of her cells. We will see the differences and similarities between her cell types and those from other living things. We will look at how she fuels her body and how it monitors its systems, as well as how a pregnancy might affect her. We will discover that DNA has a big role to play in the athlete's ability to compete, what micro-organisms can impact on her health and how she can prevent that. We will discover what different forces will slow her down during the race and find out how she can help overcome these forces, and we will be there as she passes the finishing line.

During this chapter we will cover the following Benchmarks:

- SCN 3.07a
- SCN 3.12a
- SCN 3.12b
- SCN 3.13a
- SCN 3.13b
- SCN 3.13c
- SCN 3.14a
- SCN 3.14b

Fallout!

This is the story of a survivor, told in their own words. This person has lived through a nuclear war and now he has to figure out how to continue living in a world that has changed. He needs to apply his understanding of the world in order to survive. Thinking about finding water and making sure it is clean will help us to learn about mixtures and separation techniques. As he explains his understanding of what makes up the world around him, we will learn about elements, compounds, mixtures and solutions. We will also learn about how our understanding of the properties of elements can help us organise substances into patterns like the Periodic Table. As the survivor discovers his need to stay warm, we learn about heat transfer and particle movement, as well as insulators and conductors. We look at the problems with burning fossil fuels and how we are moving forwards to use new resources. As our survivor settles into his new existence, we learn about how we could generate our own electricity and create new substances. We also discover how not all radiation is bad.

During this chapter we will cover the following Benchmarks:

- SCN 3.04a
- SCN 3.05a
- SCN 3.09a
- SCN 3.10a
- SCN 3.11b
- SCN 3.15a
- SCN 3.15b
- SCN 3.16a
- SCN 3.16b
- SCN 3.19a
- SCN 3.19b

THE SCIENTIFIC METHOD

There are four main problem-solving skills that are important to practice using when you are studying science. They will help you to understand the scientific information you are being given, not just in your classroom but in the real world too. These skills are valuable to other subjects in school and the people who will offer you a job when you leave school.

SELECTING AND PROCESSING INFORMATION

SELECTING INFORMATION

Scientists display information in lots of different ways. Some examples of the forms of scientific communication are graphs, tables and reports. It is sometimes necessary to choose information these types of displays.

How to Answer a selecting question

Using the table and your selecting skills answer the questions below.

Element	Symbol	Atomic Number
Hydrogen	H	1
Lithium	Li	3
Aluminium	Al	13
Iron	Fe	26
Lead	Pb	82

1   Which element has the highest Atomic Number?
2   Which element has the lowest Atomic Number?
3   Which element has the symbol Fe?

Let's look at question 1: to answer this question we need to find the section of the table that has the information about Atomic Number. For this table it is the last column that has this information – you can tell because the heading explains what the numbers stand for. Reading down the column, look for the highest number: 82.

You also need to know what elements you are looking at. The first column shows this information so reading down the last column to find the highest number and then moving along to the column that has the element name we can see the answer is Lead.

The same process is used to select the answer for Question 2, except this time you are selecting the smallest number (1) and then reading along the row to find the name: Hydrogen.

Question 3 is looking for different information: this time you need to find the information about the symbol. So looking to find the heading 'Symbol', you read down that column until you find the one you are looking for, Fe. Then, as with the other two questions, you look along to the element name and find Iron.

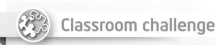

Classroom challenge

Using your **selecting skills** answer the questions about the table below.

Chapter	Chapter Title	Pages
21	Taste and Smell	202–212
22	The Brain	213–223
23	Skin, Muscle and Bone	224–233
24	Heart and Lungs	234–242
25	Immune System	243–254
26	Hygiene and Health	255–263
27	Nutrition	264–289
28	Drugs and your Body	290–315

1   What chapter is called Drugs and your body?
2   What is the chapter title for Chapter 22?
3   What page does Chapter 24 start on?
4   How many pages are in the Chapter about Nutrition?
5   If you were reading page 206:
    a   What chapter would you be reading?
    b   What would you be reading about?

PROCESSING INFORMATION

When you take numbers or values and turn them into another form of information, that is called processing. There are so many different types of processing questions that you could get in science that it would be impossible to explain how to complete them all so we will work on the two most common problems you could be asked: calculating an average and changing the form of information such as turning a table into a graph, or a graph into a table.

Calculating an average

This is used when there is more than one set of data and we want to be accurate with our answer. You will have used this calculation in your maths class. It is called the **mean average** and it is a two-step calculation.

Use your **processing skills** to calculate the average number of bubbles that are produced from the experiment.

Metal	Number of Bubbles Produced
Calcium	17
Zinc	10
Copper	3
Gold	0

The first thing you need to do it is to take all the numbers in the table and add them together.

17 + 10 + 3 + 0 = 30 bubbles

Once you have added them together you need to divide them by the number of values you had to start with, in this case 4.

30 ÷ 4 = 7.5 bubbles

This means that for this experiment results table, the average number of bubbles produced is 7.5 bubbles.

 Classroom challenge

Using this information, your **processing skills** and the data provided, calculate the average for each question.

1 What is the average volume of gas produced in ml?

Experiment 1	Volume of gas (ml)
1	23
2	26
3	31
4	21

2 What is the average height (cm) of pupils in Mrs Sharp's class?

Pupil Name	Height (cm)
Jessica	144
William	146
Jacob	132
Jasmine	145

3 What is the average test score (%) for the pupils in Mr McKellan's class?

Pupil Name	Test Score (%)
Rose	92
Amy	76
Martha	44
Micky	79
John	81
Donna	47

4 What is the average number of bubbles produced in the reaction between chalk and acid?

Time (s)	Number of bubbles
0	0
30	4
60	7
90	9

5 a What is the average rainfall per year? (**2 answers required**)
   b What is the average rainfall (mm) for each month, across both years?
     (**12 answers required**)

Month	Rainfall (mm) – 2017	Rainfall (mm) – 2018
January	183	100
February	90	143
March	98	127
April	86	63
May	46	53
June	71	153
July	81	110
August	107	147
September	173	141
October	163	179
November	160	164
December	131	147

Processing graphs

Drawing a graph is another skill you will need in science. It is considered a processing skill because you are taking information that appears in one form and changing it into another. There are lots of different types of graphs that can be drawn, but most of the time it will be a bar graph (for discrete data) or a line graph (for continuous data).

Most of the time it is simple to figure out which type of graph you should use.

If there are two sets of numbers in your data it should be a line graph.

If there are words and numbers then you should plot a bar graph.

These types of graph can show information in a user-friendly way. Graphs in science are set up using an x-axis and a y-axis, just like they are in maths.

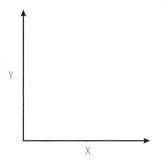

When drawing a bar graph, start off with the x-axis and y-axis

The headings from the table should be placed along each axis. The heading in the left-hand column of the table (the independent variable data) should be placed on the x-axis. The heading in the right-hand column of the table (the dependent variable data) should be placed on the y-axis, together with an appropriate scale. You should use a scale that starts at 0 and goes past the largest number of the data in the data table and you should always use a ruler!

Once you have organised your scale you should label your axis so it is easy to see what the numbers on your scale mean. Without labels your graph doesn't actually explain anything!

Classroom challenge

1 Using your **processing skills** and all the tables in this section, draw the most appropriate graph for each set of data.
2 Using your **processing skills** turn each of the graphs below into a table. Remember to include the correct headings.

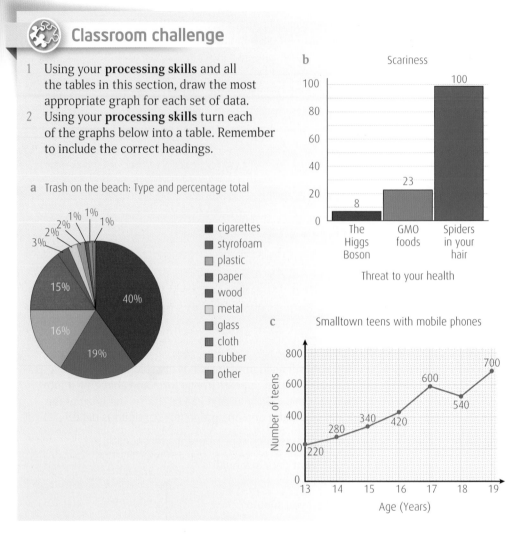

a Trash on the beach: Type and percentage total

b Scariness

c Smalltown teens with mobile phones

PREDICTING SKILLS

Predicting might seem like guessing, but in science it is possible to use your understanding of the science involved to help figure out what might happen in an experiment. It is easiest to see this with a table of data.

Temperature (°C)	Mass of Salt dissolved in 500 ml of water (g)
10	20
20	42
30	64
40	87
50	

The first thing to do when tackling this kind of problem is to start looking for a pattern. Reading down the temperature column, you can see that each of the numbers is increasing. 10 increases to 20, 20 increases to 30. It is an increase of 10 every time.

The mass of salt is increasing too. the numbers increase from 20 to 42 and from 42 to 64 – this is a increase of 22 each time. The next increase is larger, because it goes from 64 to 87 which is an increase of 23. This is a pattern and you can use that to predict what the next value would be. It makes sense that the next value would increase again by 23 or more. Answers to predicting questions will have a range of answers so you don't have to predict the exact answer, just make sure your answer falls within the answer range – any answer over 110 would be a sensibly predicted answer.

 ## Classroom challenge

Using your **predicting skills** fill in the missing values to the following tables.

1

Mass of Magnesium (g)	Time taken to fully react with acid (seconds)
0.5	
1	26
15	32
2.0	39
2.5	47

2

Mass (g)	Extension (mm)
0	0
100	5
200	9
300	
400	20
500	24
600	30

3

Water Depth (meters)	Temperature (°C)
50	
75	15
100	12
150	
200	4

4

Time (minutes)	Volume (ml)
20	800
60	600
80	
100	600
120	800
140	1200

HOW TO WRITE A LAB REPORT

There is a standard method for writing a scientific lab report. It is part of the scientific method and it is important to know how to do it correctly.

THE AIM

Most lab reports start with an **aim** that reads 'To investigate . . .'

The point of the aim is to tell other scientists why the experiment or investigation was carried out. When writing aims for your own experiments, ask yourself 'What was I trying to find out?'

Independent and dependent variables

When writing an aim it can be helpful to think about the experimental variables. Let's look at an example.

Aim: To investigate the effect of temperature on rate of reaction.

The aim tells us what was changed during the investigation: *the effect of temperature* tells us that the experimenter changed the temperature. Therefore, temperature is the **independent variable**.

The independent variable is the part of the experiment that the investigator controls. For this investigation, the scientist is in charge of the temperature. In order to see if temperature has any effect on the experiment, they will need to try a range of temperatures to give a wide range of results to analyse.

The last part of the aim tells us what the investigator is measuring. Here the scientist is studying the *rate of reaction* – looking to see if changing the temperature makes the reaction faster or slower. This part of the experiment is known as the **dependent variable**. The dependent variable changes depending on what the investigator does to the independent variable.

Now that you know more about independent and dependent variables, have a go at writing your own aims.

 Classroom challenge

Try it yourself – Aims

Instructions

1   Using the following independent and dependent variables write your own experimental aims.
    a   Independent – surface area
        Dependent – reaction rate

b   Independent – height
    Dependent – speed of trolley
c   Independent – reactivity
    Dependent – voltage produced

As you can see from this exercise, aims are easy to write as long as you know your variables!

It works the other way around too. If you are given an aim, finding the variables is quite simple.

2   Use different coloured pens to underline the independent and dependent variable in the following aims. They get harder as you go down the list. Just remember to look for what you would need to change and what you would need to measure. Be careful though, independent and dependent variables are not always written in that order.
    a   To investigate the effect of hydrochloric acid concentration on the speed of a reaction.
    b   To find out how the air temperature affects the rate at which grass grows.
    c   To find out how the number of batteries connected to a bulb affects the brightness of the bulb.
    d   To find out how the speed of a trolley rolling down a slope is affected by the angle of the slope.
    e   To investigate if changing the shape of a container affects the volume of gas produced.
    f   To investigate if voltage is affected by size of metal strip.
    g   To investigate the effect of ultraviolet light on the growth of plants.
    h   To find out the best concentration of carbon dioxide for plants to carry out photosynthesis.

Controlled variables

There are other variables to think about in a scientific experiment. All science should be fair (valid) and unbiased and experiments should always be repeatable. In order for scientific experiments to be valid, investigators must try to minimise the effects of factors that are not under study.

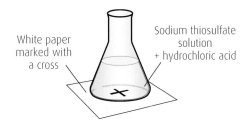

White paper marked with a cross

Sodium thiosulfate solution + hydrochloric acid

Thinking about controlled variables in an example experiment

Consider again the example aim: To investigate the effect of temperature on rate of reaction.

There are four things that can affect the rate of a reaction: temperature, chemical concentration, surface area and the use of a catalyst (page 185). In order for the experiment to be fair, the experimenter must ensure that none of these factors impacts on the experiment. These factors are called **constant** or **controlled variables**.

Constant variables need to be closely monitored, so they are the same every time the experiment is repeated. This gives a **fair test**.

The diagram shows an experimental set-up. The experimental set-up is an important part of the lab report but we'll cover this section later in the chapter.

The black cross is easy to see through the liquid in the flask at the start of the experiment and will become invisible when the experiment is complete. We know that colour change is a sign that a reaction has taken place. The speed at which the colour change occurs is a measure of the rate of the reaction.

What factors need to stay the same in this experiment? We know about the important factors that affect reaction rate. Let's identify how we could keep these the same every time we repeat the experiment.

Concentration

This experiment uses hydrochloric acid. Exactly the same type of acid must be used every time. In this case, 1 M hydrochloric acid is used. This concentration must stay the same or it will not be clear whether a change in the rate of reaction is due to a change in temperature or a change in the acid. We say that the acid concentration needs to be kept **constant**.

Surface area

The diagram also shows that sodium thiosulfate solution is used in the experiment. It would be up to the investigator to decide whether to use lumps or powder, and how much to use. These factors must be kept constant to give a fair test.

Catalyst

No other chemical is used in this reaction. This must stay the same for every repeat of the experiment to make sure it is fair.

 Classroom challenge

Identifying constant variables

Now it's your turn to identify the constant variables in the following experiments.

1 To investigate the effect of acid concentration on reaction rate.

2 To investigate the effect of surface area on reaction rate.

When writing your own lab reports, after considering the aim of your experiment and all your variables, you can fill in the top two sections of the lab-report template (see page 30).

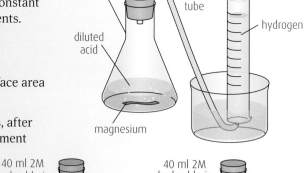

conical flask

measuring cylinder

delivery tube

hydrogen

diluted acid

magnesium

40 ml 2M hydrochloric acid

25 g marble excess

123.45 g

40 ml 2M hydrochloric acid

123.45 g

Method

The **method** section is vital to the lab report. Without an accurate method section, other scientists cannot carry out the experiment. Scientific ideas can only be accepted when others test a theory and find the same results – over and over again.

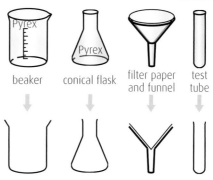

beaker   conical flask   filter paper and funnel   test tube

The method usually includes a labelled scientific diagram. Having a diagram makes it easier to follow the instructions. It also lets other scientists know what equipment they will need in order to carry out the experiment.

Use simplified versions of equipment in your drawings

Scientific diagrams are simple; they are not meant to be works of art. Use clean, clear lines, drawn using a ruler when appropriate. Always label diagrams clearly.

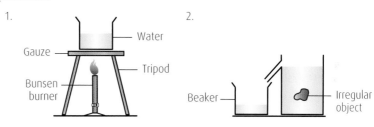

Use simple line versions of much more complicated scientific equipment. Make sure every piece of equipment is labelled clearly, so the reader can tell what everything is.

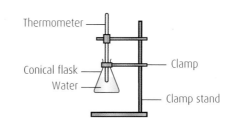

 Classroom challenge

Practise drawing scientific equipment

1   Draw a scientific diagram of each of the following pieces of equipment, which are commonly found in science laboratories.
- Measuring cylinder
- Beaker
- Test tube
- Tripod
- Bunsen burner
- Thermometer
- Test-tube rack
- Spatula
- Funnel
- Glass stirring rod

2   Now draw a complete apparatus set-up to carry out each of the following procedures.
   a   To heat up water
   b   To measure the temperature of a mixture of acid and magnesium metal
   c   To mix together two different liquids

Instructions

Having completed a diagram for the experiment, it is time to continue with the method by writing a list of **instructions** so other scientists can carry out the experiment.

These instructions should be very clear and concise, telling the reader exactly what needs to be done at each stage. It must include the quantities of any materials that are needed and the actions that should be taken.

 Did you know?

Using the right language

Scientific methods are written in a way that means they can be followed easily. Even if the names of the chemicals are hard to say or the equipment is unfamiliar, the reader should still be able to figure out how to do the experiment.

Never include words like *I, my, we, our, you* and *your*. This is because scientific reports use impersonal language. They are also written in the past tense as this makes them easier to follow.

Consider again the example investigation into the effect of temperature on reaction rate.

1   Put 10 cm³ of sodium thiosulfate solution and 40 cm³ of water into a conical flask. Measure 5 cm³ of dilute hydrochloric acid in a small measuring cylinder.
2   Warm the thiosulfate solution in the flask if necessary to bring it to the required temperature. The object is to repeat the experiment five times at different temperatures in the range 15–55 °C.
3   Put the conical flask over a piece of paper with a cross drawn on it.
4   Add the acid and start the clock. Swirl the flask to mix the solutions and place it back on the cross. Note the initial temperature of the mixture.

 Classroom challenge

Practise writing instructions

Write a list of instructions in scientific style (and draw a scientific drawing) for each of the following scenarios.

1   Making a cup of tea
2   Brushing your teeth
3   Boiling an egg
4   Boiling water using a Bunsen burner
5   Filtering sand out of sandy water

Safety!

All experiments should be carried out with safety in mind. It is important to follow instructions carefully to avoid risks.

This is also true outside the lab. Wherever you are, it's important to read the rules and understand why they are there. Let's think about some simple rules that are designed to keep people safe.

 **No Diving**    **No Running**

Let's look at the two pool rules:

- No diving – because the pool isn't deep enough. If you bang your head on the bottom of the pool, you could hurt your neck or even drown.
- No running – because the poolside is slippery when wet. You fall and hurt yourself.

When you are writing a lab report, consider any problems that could arise if the person doing the experiment isn't careful. Think about all the ways you can stop them from hurting themselves and note these in the instructions.

Consider the risks involved in the experiment to look at the effect of temperature on reaction rate experiment.

One of the chemicals used is hydrochloric acid. It is known to be hazardous.

Risk assessment for HCl

Risk	Possible injury
Acids are corrosive	Burns and irritation if in contact with skin

All acids are corrosive, which means that they burn when they touch skin. This is a risk because the person carrying out the experiment may not know that hydrochloric acid is dangerous or how to handle it safely. It is your job, as the lab-report author, to alert the reader to this danger and to give instructions about what to do if they spill it on their hands.

Directions for safe use of HCl

Risk	Possible injury	Prevention
Acids are corrosive	Burns and irritation if in contact with skin	Measure dilute HCl carefully. Wear safety goggles

Classroom challenge

Assessing risk

Think again about the methods you wrote previously.

1 Making a cup of tea
2 Brushing your teeth
3 Boiling an egg
4 Boiling water using a Bunsen burner
5 Filtering sand out of sandy water

Identify any risks, possible injuries that could happen and any preventative measures that the person carrying out the instructions should know.

If you have filled out the aim, variables, safety considerations, diagram and method sections of the lap report template (page 30), you are now halfway through! The front page of the lab-report template should be complete and you are now ready to carry out the experiment.

 Classroom challenge

Practice report writing

Practice all of the **lab-report writing skills** you have tried so far!

> *Aim:* *To investigate the effect of changing the mass of chalk added to acid on volume of gas given off*

Variables to keep the same: _____

_____

Possible risks: _____

_____

Ways to reduce risks: _____

_____

Diagram of experiment:

Aim: To investigate how the volume of water in a beaker affects the temperature increase when heated above a Bunsen flame for 1 minute.

Variables to keep the same: --

Possible risks: --

Ways to reduce risks: --

Diagram of experiment:

Results

All successful experiments have results. These can be **observations or numerical** data depending on the aim of the experiment. To help you make sense of your data, your results need to be organised. This is most commonly done as a **table of results**.

Tables should be easy to follow with a format that clearly shows what the information means.

Always use correct column headings with units (where appropriate) so you remember and any reader knows exactly what was being measured.

Table 25 Results for the investigation into the effect of temperature on reaction rate

Temperature (°C)	Time taken for cross to disappear (seconds)
10	195
20	107
30	61
40	35
50	17
60	9

Table 25 is simple and is easy to read. It shows what measurements were taken. But one set of results isn't very **reliable**. Experiments should always be carried out more than once, usually three times, and then an **average** calculated (see Table 26). This is the best way to make sure results are reliable.

Table 26 Some more reliable results, with average values

Temperature (°C)	Time taken for cross to disappear (seconds)			
	1	2	3	Average
10	196	194	196	195.3
20	95	93	94	94
30	61	63	59	61
40	28	30	28	28.7
50	15	14	13	14
60	7	7	6	6.7

Calculating an average

Scientists need to be able to trust their experimental data and, if experiments are carried out correctly, other scientists should find the same data when they do the same experiments. The more times a theory is demonstrated, the more trusted the information. This is why scientists repeat experiments.

There will always be slight differences between repeat sets of results. Calculating the average helps to minimise the effect of the differences.

 Did you know?

Mean, median and mode

There are different types of averages that you will learn about in maths: the mean, median and mode.

To calculate the **mean average** you add up the data repeats for the individual experiment and then divide by the number of sets of results.

Let's look again at the Table 26. At 5 °C three repeats were carried out. The results were: 290, 291 and 289.

> To find the average, first add the results together.
>
> 290 + 291 + 289 = 870
>
> To get the average we have to divide it by 3.
>
> 870 ÷ 3 = 290

The average is 290 seconds for the cross to disappear at 5°C.

When calculating an average, you need to remember to divide the total by the number of experiments. If four repeats were done, you would add all four results together and then divide by 4.

Classroom challenge

Practising calculations

Instructions

1 Double check the averages in the table on p. 24. Show all your working.
2 Copy and complete Tables 27 and 28 by calculating the averages.

Table 27

Mass of chalk added to acid (g)	Volume of gas given off (cm³)		
	Experiment 1	Experiment 2	Average
10	18	21	
20	38	39	
30	61	61	
40	85	78	
50	98	96	

Table 28

Car model	Distance driven using 1 litre of petrol (miles)		
	Experiment 1	Experiment 2	Average
Fiesta	18.0	17.6	
Polo	15.3	15.7	
Veyron	1.1	1.3	
Zafira	9.3	9.5	
Passat	7.4	7.2	

Presenting information

Patterns or **trends** in results are hard to see in a table of results. They can be seen more easily when shown in a graph.

There are a number of different graph forms that can be used, depending on the type of experiment. The two most common forms of graphs used for **presenting data** from experiments are bar and line graphs.

If you have **discrete** data then you would use a bar graph. Discrete data is information in separate groups or categories. An example is shown from an experiment to compare lather produced by different brands of washing up liquid.

The brand of washing up liquid cannot be made

Dependant variable on vertical axis

Axes both labelled, with units and scales evenly spaced out, filling at least half of the graph paper

Independant variable on horizontal axis

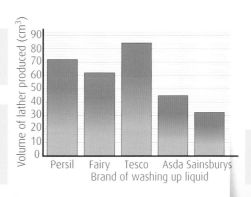

into a numerical scale, so a bar graph is appropriate. The volume of lather can be placed on a numerical scale.

If the dependent and independent variables can both be fitted into numerical scales, you would draw a line graph (sometimes called a scatter graph if the points do not fall exactly on the line). This type of graph is used for **continuous** data, where there is a minimum, a maximum and a range of values in between.

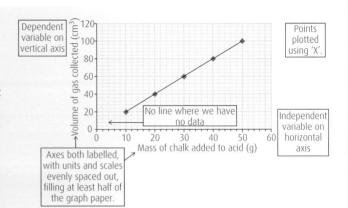

 Classroom challenge

Drawing graphs

Instructions

Using the averages you calculated in Tables 27 and 28, draw graphs of both sets of data.

Remember to include axis labels with units. Use graph paper and make sure each graph fills about half of the page.

Use Table 29 to draw a graph to complete the lab-report template.

Table 29 Table of results for an investigation into the effect of temperature on reaction rate

| Temperature (°C) | Time taken for cross to disappear (seconds) | | | |
	Experiment 1	Experiment 2	Experiment 3	Average
10	196	195	197	196
20	95	93	94	94
30	53	53	53	53
40	28	30	29	29
50	15	14	13	14
60	5	7	6	6

Conclusion

The **conclusion** should written as response to the original aim – it should answer the question you were asking by doing the experiment. The conclusion should be supported by the results of the experiment.

Your conclusion doesn't need to be incredibly long. Consider again the experiment with the aim of investigating the effect of temperature on reaction rate.

Look at the graph you have drawn from the results of this experiment (in Table 29). So, does changing the temperature have an effect on the rate of reaction (shown by the time taken for the cross to disappear)?

The answer to the question is 'yes' but you can't just write that without an explanation! You could write: 'In conclusion, changing the temperature did have an effect on the reaction rate.'

You should extend this brief conclusion by describing the effect you observed. In this experiment, as the temperature increases, the time it takes for the cross to disappear reduces, so the reaction must be going faster.

So, the ideal conclusion would read: 'In conclusion, changing the temperature did have an effect on the reaction rate. It was found that increasing the temperature increased the rate of reaction.'

This conclusion is short and to the point, but answers the question that was set in the aim.

 ## Classroom challenge

Writing conclusions

Write conclusions for the aims below. If you don't know what the science would show for these questions, you can make up your answers!

1 To investigate the effect of concentration on the speed of a reaction.
2 To find out how the air temperature affects the rate at which grass grows.
3 To find out how the number of batteries connected to a bulb affects the brightness of the bulb.
4 To find out how the speed of a trolley rolling down a slope is affected by the angle of the slope.
5 To investigate if changing the shape of a container affects the volume of gas produced.

Evaluation

This part of the lab report examines how well the experiment went and considers how to do the procedure better next time, but without changing any of the controlled variables.

The evaluation also explains what was done to minimise any errors that could have crept in.

An effective evaluation has two parts:

1 identifying a problem
2 explaining how to fix it

For the example experiment, there are a couple of things that could make the procedure better.

The investigator times how long it takes for the black cross to become invisible. A stop clock is started when the chemicals are added together and stopped when the black cross can no longer be seen.

This isn't the most accurate way to record the time taken because it relies on the person with the stop clock paying close attention and pressing the stop clock as fast as they can. Different people might press the button faster or slower, or pay close attention or be distracted, so it would be better to use the same person every time the experiment is repeated.

You could evaluate this by saying: 'Next time this experiment is done, one person should take the timing role in all repeats to make sure the reaction time of the person recording the time is always the same.'

There are other ways to measure the time taken more accurately. For example, the experiment could be recorded on video and replayed. The time taken could be read from the video time codes rather than using a person and stopwatch. This would cut down on human error and eliminate differences in reaction time between people.

Evaluations should be as detailed as possible, not short like conclusions. This is where you show off the practical knowledge you have gained by doing the experiment.

 Classroom challenge

Writing an evaluation

Refer back to your methods from the previous section.

- Making a cup of tea
- Brushing your teeth
- Boiling an egg
- Boiling water using a Bunsen burner
- Filtering sand out of sandy water

Write an evaluation about how the method could be changed to make the procedure better. Remember to identify the problem and explain how to fix it!

Your lab-report template should be complete. Keep it safe. It will help you with your lab-report tasks in the rest of the chapter.

Use the following experiment prompts to practise your **scientific communication skills**.

GERMINATION INVESTIGATION

Information

Germination is the term used to describe when seeds sprout and begin to grow.

There are many things that could affect germination. You will be growing cress on some damp cotton wool in a plastic cup dish.

Discussion

Discuss what factors may affect how many of your seeds will germinate.

Task

Your task is:

- Plan and carry out an experiment to investigate the effect the number of seeds in each cup has on the percentage of seeds which germinate within a certain time (2 or three days).

REACTION RATE INVESTIGATION

Information

Some chemical reactions are fast while others are slow.

Explosions are example of very fast chemical reactions. They take very little time.

Iron rusting is an example of a slow chemical reaction. This takes a long time.

It is possible to speed up and slow down chemical reactions.

Chemicals in solutions may react with each other. One factor that can change the speed of a chemical reaction like this, is the concentration of the chemicals reacting. The concentration tells us how much of the chemical is dissolved in water. The more of the chemical dissolved in a certain volume, the higher the concentration. One way of measuring concentration is using percentage. The higher the percentage, the higher the concentration.

Demonstration

Your teacher will demonstrate what happens when two chemicals, A and B, are mixed together.

Discussion

Discuss how you could measure and compare the speed of the chemical reaction using different concentrations of solution B.

Equipment

The equipment available to you is:

- Solution A
- Three different concentrations of solution B (5%, 10% and 15%)
- Any other equipment found in the lab.

Task

Your task is:

- Plan and carry out an experiment to investigate the effect of concentration on reaction rate.

PENDULUM INVESTIGATION

Information

Some clocks have a mass that swings back and forwards. This is called a pendulum. It allows the clock to stay accurate.

A simple pendulum can be made by tying a mass to the end of a string and allowing it to swing. The time it takes for a pendulum to make one complete swing (back and forwards) is called the period of the pendulum. In the diagram on the right, it is the time to travel from A to B, and then back to A.

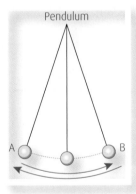

 Classroom challenge

Task

Your task is:

- Following discussion, choose one factor that you think might affect the period of a pendulum.
- Plan and carry out an experiment to investigate this factor (tip: it may be easier to time more than one swing).

LAB-REPORT TEMPLATE

Name:

TITLE:

Experimental report

Aim *(A statement that explains what your experiment will investigate)*

Variables

Independent variable:

Dependent variable:

Coritrolled variables:

Method *(A **labelled** diagram with a description of how your experiment was carried out. You should particularly describe how your **variables** were **changed** and **measured**)*

Diagram

State any **safety issues** and describe how you dealt with them

Results *(Your table of results. The column headings should contain the **units** of the measurements)*

Conclusion *(A statement that describes what the results have shown us. **This should relate to the aim**)*

Evaluation *(A statement that explains how your experiment could be improved)*

Teacher Feedback

HOW TO DO RESEARCH TASKS

Research tasks require you to use your **selecting skills**. You need to search for, select and edit **relevant** information.

There a number of places you can find information; the most easily accessible one is usually the internet. While this is an easy place to find information, it is not always reliable.

FINDING A RELIABLE SOURCE OF INFORMATION

There are number of places on the internet with lots of accessible information. Google and Wikipedia are excellent places to start your research, but they shouldn't be your only sources of information.

For information to be **reliable** it must come from a **reputable** website. What is a reputable website and how would you know? You need to think about who is writing the information; everyone is entitled to an opinion but not everyone's opinion is based on scientific fact!

- Websites that are published by educational establishments like universities (.edu) contain material that is written by experts and that is peer reviewed (assessed by other academics). Peer review is a very important tool because it lets you know that information has been tested and demonstrated to be true.
- Government websites (.gov) are usually regulated to ensure that the information is reliable.
- Some.com or.co.uk websites are reliable, but not all.

When assessing information from a website, always ask yourself these questions:

- Has someone else demonstrated the same thing?
- Do other scientists agree with this?
- Is the writer being paid to say this?

If you can't answer those questions (yes, yes, no) then you should look for another source of information.

Wiki

Wikipedia content can be written by anyone who wants to add an article – the contributors don't have to be experts. The material can be edited by others, so a certain level of accuracy comes from this collaboration. Wiki also has staff who check facts, but this process isn't always up to date.

Wikipedia requires content to be **referenced**, so you can find out who said a fact first and decide if they are a reliable source of information.

In the same way that Wikipedia references all of its sources of information so should you: **always record where you found your information**.

Did you know?

Plagiarism

Plagiarism is when you take someone else's work and pretend it is your own. This includes copying your friend's homework or lifting text from books or the internet.

Exam boards have been known to fail pupils who are caught cheating in this way. Universities and colleges have expelled students who have plagiarised work. People can be prosecuted with copyright infringement if they plagiarise published works.

It can be tempting to copy someone else's work, but you should always put information in your own words and tell your reader where the information came from!

References should always include as much information as possible. When using the internet, the easiest thing to do is to click on the address bar and copy and paste the entire link into your work. This means that the reader can find the exact same page if they wish to follow up on your source.

For example, Tim Peake is a British astronaut who has one son and enjoys skiing. (https://www.esa.int/esaKIDSen/SEMD42DR5GG_LifeinSpace_0.html)

It wouldn't be enough just to write www.esa.int, because the reader wouldn't be able to find the exact page that the information came from.

Books are slightly different. If the information about Tim Peake came from a book the reference would have to include the book's title, author, page number and **ISBN number**. For example:

Ask an Astronaut: My Guide to Life in Space (Official Tim Peake Book), Tim Peake, Page 47, ISBN 9781780898179, May 2018, Cornerstone

Classroom challenge

Writing references

Instructions

Using the internet or books, answer the following questions. Make sure you write the answer in your own words and give a reference for where you found the information.

1 Why is the sky blue?
2 How do fireworks work?
3 How long should you cook a boiled egg for to make it hard?
4 How long do cats live on average?
5 Who invented the lightbulb?
6 Who was the first person to fly the entire way around the world?
7 How long does it take to get to Mars?
8 When was Winnie the Pooh written and by whom?
9 What was the biggest dinosaur in the Jurassic era?
10 What song was number one in the charts on the day you were born?

STEM CAREERS RESEARCH

The skills you have developed while studying science will be useful in a huge variety of ways. They will help you achieve at school and they will make you a desirable candidate for a college or university place or for an apprenticeship.

Employers want employees with these skills, so the Scottish Government has made science a priority in education, along with other subjects that use similar skills. These subjects are often grouped together and referred to as STEM (science, technology, engineering and maths) subjects.

Classroom challenge

Thinking ahead

Instructions

Using your **researching skills** and this section of this book, research a project from the following list. You should work in pairs or small groups to complete the task.

- To research the different STEM career options within the beauty industry, focusing on cosmetics, fragrance or skincare.
- To research the different STEM career options within the sports industry, focusing on sport engineering, sports science or sports statistics.
- To research the different STEM career options within the fashion industry focusing on material science, product pricing or sustainable fashion.
- To research the different STEM career options within the music industry focusing on audio technology, royalties analysis or audio engineering.
- To research the different STEM career options within the film industry focusing on set design, computer animation or motion capture engineering.

Present your research project to your class as a PowerPoint or verbal presentation, a poster or an informational booklet. Your presentation should include all of the following information:

- What jobs are available in the sector?
- Describe two job roles within the sector. What do these people actually do?
- What is the average salary for these jobs?
- How do you get a job like these? What is the career path? Do you need a degree, a college qualification or can you do an apprenticeship?
- What subjects would you need to study at school for a job like these?

IMPACT!

Earth; at least 7 billion human beings exist together on this small sphere of rock and water. Our home planet is nestled between mysterious Venus and smaller, cooler Mars. Earth, Venus and Mars are located in a neighbourhood of planets, the Solar System, which humans have yet to fully explore.

THE SOLAR SYSTEM

Rocks of various sizes hurtle through space. These are the leftover building blocks of planets. Some are as small as a grain of sand; others are as large as a mountain range – and there are all sizes in between. They are held in orbit, circling the Sun, just like all the planets in our Solar System. A rock, hidden deep within the asteroid belt 1 000 000 000 000 miles away from Earth, could travel all the way to hit the surface of our fragile home planet.

The outcomes and experiences for this chapter are:

By using my knowledge of our Solar System and the basic needs of living things, I can produce a reasoned argument on the likelihood of life existing elsewhere in the Universe. SCN 3-06a

I have collaborated in investigations into the effects of gravity on objects and I can predict what might happen to their weight in different situations on Earth and in space. SCN 3-08a

 What's coming up?

- Discovering the structure of the Solar System
- Learning about the effects of gravity

THE STRUCTURE OF THE SOLAR SYSTEM

Our home, planet Earth, sits in space within a group of objects that are all bound together by the force due to **gravity**. This group is known collectively as the **Solar System**.

 DON'T FORGET

My **V**ery **E**asy **M**ethod **J**ust **S**peeds **U**p **N**aming **(P**lanets**)** can help you to remember the order of the planets from the Sun outwards.

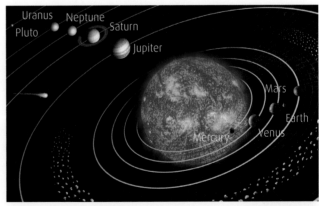

The Solar System: Mercury, Venus, Earth, Mars, Jupiter, Saturn, Uranus and Neptune (and Pluto) orbit the Sun

Orbits

Earth is one of eight **planets** that move around the Sun, a **star**. The Sun is located at the centre of the **Solar System**. The near circular motion of a planet around the Sun is called an **orbit**. The time that it takes a planet to orbit around the star is called a **year**.

Earth's orbit around the Sun

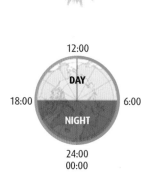

The Earth spins on its axis

While the planets orbit the star, each one is also spinning on its own axis. The time that it takes for a planet to spin one complete revolution is called a **day**. The eight different planets all have different lengths of **years** and **days** as shown in Table 1.

Table 1 Length of years and days on different planets

	Mercury	Venus	Earth	Mars	Jupiter	Saturn	Uranus	Neptune
Length of year (Earth days)	87.6	226.3	365	686.2	4328.9	10752.9	30663.65	60152
Length of day (hours)	1407.6	5832	24	24.72 .	9.84	10.56	17.28	17.28

 Classroom challenge

Hours, days and years

You can use the information in Table 1 in calculations. When you carry out calculations you are using your **processing skills**. You can also apply knowledge you already know to a question in order to find new information.

For example: 2 years on Venus is

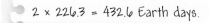

2 × 226.3 = 432.6 Earth days.

Instructions

Use your **processing skills** to answer the following questions.

Questions

1 How many Earth days is 1 year on Jupiter?
2 How many hours is 1 day on Mars?
3 Which planet has the longest day?
4 Which planet has the shortest year?
5 How many Earth days would
 2 years on Uranus be?
6 How many Earth days would
 5 years on Mercury be?
7 How many hours would there be in
 6 days on Neptune?
8 How many hours would there be in
 15 days on Jupiter?
9 How many hours would there be in
 2 years on Saturn?
10 How many hours would there be in 7 years on Earth?

 ## Classroom challenge

Drawing a bar graph

Then use this scale to draw a bar for each planet. The example bar graph shows the
length of year on five of the different planets.

Instructions

Using Table 1 and the example bar chart to guide you, draw a bar graph for the length of
a day for Earth, Mars, Jupiter, Saturn and Neptune. It should take up at least half a sheet
of graph paper and be drawn with a ruler.

Length of year on different planets

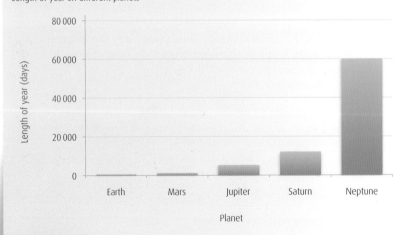

Moons

If you look closely at the image of our Solar System on page 38, you may notice that some of the planets have small objects moving around them. The smaller bodies that orbit around a **planet** are called **moons**. One moon orbits the Earth. Some planets have many more moons and others have none at all.

View of Earth from its moon

The Sun

The star at the centre of the Solar System, which we call the Sun, is a huge sphere of Hydrogen and Helium gas. Very powerful nuclear reactions take place at the centre of the Sun, resulting in release of massive amounts of light and heat energy. Without this light and heat, life on Earth would not exist!

Nuclear reactions take place deep within the Sun

Asteroids

As well as the star at the centre of the Solar System and the planets and the moons that orbit it, there are some other very important objects in space that you should know about.

If you look at the area of space between the planets Mars and Jupiter, you will see the **asteroid belt**. The asteroid belt is an orbit full of billions of rocks and debris that were left over from the formation of the Solar System over 4 billion years ago. These space rocks, which we call **asteroids**, range in size from microscopic to the size of a mountain.

Asteroids can crash into planets

Table 2 Definitions of celestial objects

Object	Definition
Star	Ball of gas, held together by gravity, with a centre that is incredibly hot and emits visible light and other radiation
Planet	A spherical object that orbits a Sun and is not a satellite of another object
Moon	A natural satellite of a planet
Satellite	An object, natural or made by humans, that orbits around a planet or a star
Asteroid	A small rocky body that orbits a Sun

Occasionally, in the chaos of space debris asteroids collide and are knocked out of their orbits. They may hurtle through space until they collide with a planet. When an asteroid knocks into a planet, it can leave a **crater** or mark on the surface, and some collisions have had devastating effects! It is thought that the dinosaurs were wiped out as a result of a massive asteroid collision with Earth about 65 million years ago.

Oort cloud

Finally, to complete our tour of the Solar System, we must consider the **Oort cloud**. This 'cloud' is found at the outer edge of our Solar System. It is a huge orbit of countless icy rocks. **Comets** are thought to originate from this region of space.

Occasionally, like asteroids, comets can be knocked out of their remote orbits and be redirected towards the inner Solar System. As a comet approaches the Sun, the ice around the rock begins to melt, resulting in the appearance of a beautiful trailing tail. Comets can also collide with planets, leaving a crater.

A comet called Shoemaker-Levy impacted with Jupiter

 Classroom challenge

Classifying planets

Did you know that, until recently, scientists claimed that there were nine planets? Can you find out why this changed?

Instructions

Using the resources available to you, follow these steps to write a short report of 80–100 words titled '**Pluto**'.

1 Start by finding out the names of the nine previously identified planets.
2 Describe the criteria an object in space must meet to be considered a planet.
3 Now conclude why the 'ninth planet' no longer has this status.

The planets in our Solar System are wonderfully different places. Each world has varied characteristics that give very different environments, which have fascinated astronomers and scientists for hundreds of years. The data in Table 3 shows us some of the important characteristics of each of the planets.

Table 3 Comparing planetary characteristics

Planets	Distance from the Sun (km)	Diameter (km)	Time to spin on axis (a planetary day in Earth days, hours or minutes)	Time to orbit Sun (a year in Earth days or years)	Gravity (Earth = 1)	Average temperature (°C)	Contents of atmosphere	Number of known moons
Mercury	57 900 000	4878	59 days	88 days	0.38	−183–427 °C	Sodium, helium	0
Venus	108 160 000	12 104	243 days	224 days	0.9	480 °C	Carbon dioxide (96%), nitrogen (3.5%)	0
Earth	149 600 000	12 756	23 hour 56 mins	365.25 days	1	14 °C	Nitrogen (77%), oxygen (21%)	1
Mars	227 936 640	6794	24 hours 37 mins	687 days	0.38	−63 °C	Carbon dioxide (95.3%), argon	2
Jupiter	778 369 000	142 984	9 hours 55 mins	11.86 years	2.64	−130 °C	Hydrogen, helium	66
Saturn	1 427 034 000	120 536	10 hours 39 mins	29 years	1.16	−130 °C	Hydrogen, helium	62
Uranus	2 870 658 186	51 118	17 hours 14 mins	84 years	1.11	−200 °C	Hydrogen, helium, methane	27
Neptune	4 496 976 000	49 532	16 hours 7 mins	164.8 years	1.21	−200 °C	Hydrogen, helium, methane	13

 Classroom challenge

Comparing planets

Questions

Read the table about the different planets and use your **selecting skills** to answer questions 1–4.

1   Which planet has a diameter that is most similar to Earth's?
2   Using the table, describe any one major difference this planet has compared to Earth.
3   Write a list of the planets in order of diameter, starting with the largest.
4   Describe what is strange about the length of a day and the length of a year on Venus.
5   Venus is the warmest planet in the Solar System, yet is further from the Sun than Mercury. Using your library resources or the internet and your **researching skills** to find out why this is.
6   Using your **processing skills**, draw a bar graph showing the number of moons that orbit each planet.

7   By **analysing** the data can you describe a relationship (link) between the distance a planet is from the Sun and the time it takes to complete an orbit of the Sun (orbital period)?

Using your **researching skills** and library resources or the internet, complete these tasks.

8   Why it is difficult to detect exoplanets?
9   Explain why the exoplanet Kepler 186f is of particular interest to scientists.
10 What facts can you find out about Kepler 186f (distance from Earth, length of a year, average surface temperature, for example)?

PLANETS OF THE SOLAR SYSTEM

 Classroom challenge

Making a Solar System diagram

Using the images in the diagram to help you, draw the Solar System. Make sure your planets are in the correct order working outwards from the Sun and are the right size relative to each other. Use a ruler to accurately measure the **diameter** of each of the planets in the diagram. Label your drawing clearly. Add colour to your diagram to give an accurate representation of how we see the Solar System.

Add a small description of each planet to your diagram.

Mercury   Venus   Earth

Mars   Jupiter   Saturn

Uranus   Neptune   Pluto

 **TEACHING NOTES**

Find this image as a worksheet for class use at www.brightredpublishing.co.uk

GRAVITY

An asteroid's path through the Solar System is continually shaped by gravity. Gravity is a force of attraction that pulls masses together – the larger the mass, the larger the gravitational pull. As an asteroid draws nearer to a planet, the strength of the gravitational pull increases and the effect on the asteroid's path becomes more pronounced.

The force due to gravity on each of the eight planets in our Solar System is different. Gravity is an attractive force between the centres of two bodies, such as a planet and an object on the surface of the planet, or between the Sun and a planet, for example.

On Earth, gravity is a force which attracts an object to the centre of the Earth. Gravity is also experienced on the other planets. Gravity is linked to the mass of an object, so planets of different masses have different forces of gravity.

Weight, measured in Newtons, is a measurement of this force due to gravity. This means that you weigh more on Earth than you would on Mars! Mass is measured in kilograms (kg).

Gravity calculations

We can use a simple mathematical equation to calculate how much you would weigh on Earth and how much you would weigh on other planets.

> weight = mass × gravity
>
> or
>
> W = m × G

DON'T FORGET

When you 'weigh' yourself you are really measuring your mass, *not* your weight.

You take your mass, measured in kilograms (kg), and multiply it by the gravity on the planet in question.

 How does that work?

Using $W = m \times G$

Here we will calculate the weight of an object on two planets using the formula $W = m \times G$.

The following example is based on a person who has a mass of 41 kg on Earth, where the force of gravity is 10 N/kg. The force of gravity on Mars is 4 N/kg.

> Earth
>
> W = 41 kg × 10 N/kg
>
> weight = 410 N

Mars

$W = 41\,Kg \times 4\,N/kg$

Weight $= 164\,N$

To calculate the mass of an object if you are given the weight and a value for gravity, you can use the same equation but change it around to give $m = W/G$.

Earth

$m = 410\,N/10\,N/kg$

mass $= 41\,kg$

Mars

$m = 164\,N/4\,N/kg$

mass $= 41\,kg$

Download the Homework Helpers for an extra activity on using the $W = m \times G$ formula.

Classroom challenge

Gravity on different planets

Instructions

Now using your **processing skills** calculate your weight on a planet of your choice. Repeat for four friends or family members on four other planets. Values for gravity on different planets are given in Table 4.

Use your **processing skills** in a different way to record the answers to your calculations in a table of results. Finally, **process** your data into a graph. Make sure you remember to include axis labels with units.

DON'T FORGET

Remember that when you are using equations like $m = W/G$ the letters represent numbers. You can find the numbers you need from the question you are answering or in the table of information you are given.

Table 4 Surface gravity on different planets

Planet	Surface gravity (N/kg)
Mercury	4
Venus	9
Earth	10
Mars	4
Jupiter	25
Saturn	10
Uranus	10
Neptune	11

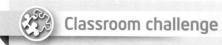 **Classroom challenge**

Calculating weight and mass

Instructions

Using Table 4 and the 'How does that work?' section, answer the questions below.

For questions 1–5 the mass of James is 39 kg.

For questions 6–12 Lauren's weight on Earth is 45 kg.

For questions 13–15 you will need to use your **processing skills**.

Questions

Calculate James' weight on

1 Uranus
2 Saturn
3 Mercury
4 Venus
5 Neptune.

Calculate Lauren's mass on

6 Mercury
7 Venus
8 Earth
9 Mars
10 Jupiter
11 Saturn
12 Uranus.

13 Katie's mass on Earth is 45 kg. On which planet would she weigh the most?
14 Andrew has a weight of 560 N on Earth. On which planet would he weigh the least?
15 Graeme has a mass of 50 kg. On which planet would his weight be 550 N?

Gravity and distance

The gravitational field strength decreases as the distance from a planet's surface increases. A person on the peak of Mount Everest weighs slightly less (99.7%) than they would at sea level.

It is often said that astronauts who work on board the International Space Station, orbiting at an altitude of around 400 km above the surface of the Earth, are 'weightless'. However, they still weigh around 90% of their weight at sea level. Their *apparent* weightlessness is due to the station being in a free-fall orbit around the Earth, which means that the astronaut and the shuttle are moving towards the Earth with the same acceleration because the only force acting upon them both is the gravitational pull of the planet below them.

The graph on page 48 shows how Earth's gravitational field strength changes as altitude above sea level changes.

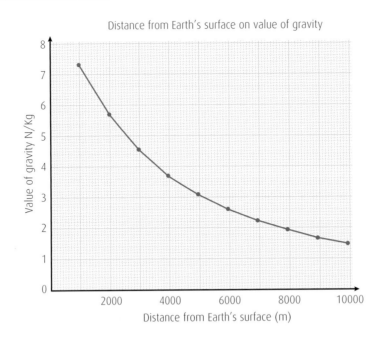

Distance from Earth's surface on value of gravity

Value of gravity N/Kg (vertical axis)

Distance from Earth's surface (m) (horizontal axis)

 Classroom challenge

Solving gravity problems

Sometimes when we are studying topics like space, the information we are provided with seems very complicated. Even though the graph and Table 4 look difficult to understand, you may be surprised by how easy they are to use when answering questions. Reading graphs is a problem-solving skill called '**selecting**'. Your brain is a problem-solving machine, just like a calculator.

Instructions

To solve the following problems you need to look at the numbers on the graph and figure out what they mean.

Questions

Use your **selecting skills** to find the value of gravity at these distances from the surface of the Earth:

1　2000 km
2　8000 km
3　4000 km
4　10 000 km.

Instructions

Now that you have practised using the graph to find simple numbers, you can try something a little harder.

Questions

5   How far from the Earth's surface would you be if the value of gravity is 2.6 N/Kg?
6   How far from the Earth's surface would you be if the value of gravity is 7.33 N/Kg?

Instructions

When you are looking at graphs, you need to think about the **scale** of each axis. In this graph each division along the bottom represents 1000 km. Using this information, you need to think about where the **data points** on the graph sit.

Questions

7   When the value of gravity is 2.23 N/Kg how far from the Earth's surface are you?
8   When the value of gravity is 4.53 N/Kg how far from the Earth's surface are you?

Instructions

To answer the following questions, you will need to take what you have learned from the graph and apply it to your other knowledge, this is called **processing**.

Questions

9   Would you weigh more or less if you were at the top of Mount Everest compared to sea level?
10 Would being at the bottom of the ocean affect your weight?
11 Do you think your weight would be different in deep space? Explain your answer.
12 Using your **predicting skills** determine the value of gravity when you are 12 000 km from the Earth's surface.

The asteroid did not slow down on its path. It kept going on its course, travelling past the planets and interacting with their gravitational pulls, and was pulled closer and closer to the Sun. The Earth was in its path. Nothing could be done to change what happened next.

Classroom challenge

Making a table of results

For this task you will have to use your **processing skills**. You have practised drawing graphs from tables of data, but can you make a table from a graph?

Taking information from a graph and understanding and explaining what the graph means is a **processing skill**. Using the graph on page 48, make a table of results. Remember that tables should have headings with units where appropriate. All table lines should be drawn with a ruler and you should include *all* the data points noted in the graph.

THE EARTH

The Earth, known as the 'blue planet', it is approximately 4.45 billion years old.

Did you know?

The Earth is a rock planet

Planet Earth: fact file

Diameter: 12 756 km / 7926 miles
Distance from the Sun: 149.6 million km / 93 million miles
One orbit = 365.26 Earth days
Average surface temperature: 15 °C / 59 °F
Temperature range: −90 °C to +58 °C
Number of moons: 1

The outcomes and experiences for this chapter are:

I can sample and identify living things from different habitats to compare their biodiversity and can suggest reasons for their distribution. SCN 3–01a

I have collaborated on investigations into the process of photosynthesis and I can demonstrate my understanding of why plants are vital to sustaining life on Earth. SCN 3–02a

Through investigations and based on experimental evidence, I can explain the use of different types of chemicals in agriculture and their alternatives and can evaluate their potential impact on the world's food production. SCN 3–03a

I can explain some of the processes which contribute to climate change and discuss the possible impact of atmospheric change on the survival of living things. SCN 3–05b

I can participate in practical activities to extract useful substances from natural resources. SCN 3–17b

What's coming up?

- Looking at Earth
- Discovering the rock cycle
- Learning about biodiversity
- Finding out about photosynthesis
- Learning about agriculture
- Exploring climate change
- Discovering renewables

STRUCTURE OF THE EARTH

The Earth's internal structure is made of three different parts:

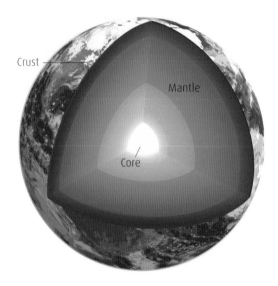

Crust

Mantle

Core

A diagram of the internal structure of the Earth

- The **core** is made of molten iron. It is the part at the very centre of our planet. The core is so hot that the iron is completely melted and swirls around as the Earth spins on its **axis**.
- The **mantle** is made up of silicate rock, which is mostly solid but has a liquid layer where the mantle meets the crust. The rock is organised into seven different plates, called tectonic plates, which move around each other, causing earthquakes and making mountains, volcanoes and valleys.
- The **crust** is a thin layer that covers the entire surface of the Earth. This is where plants grow and animals live. Everything that is needed for life on Earth is found in the **crust**. The planet is mostly covered in water; around 70% of the surface of Earth is covered in oceans. There are different types of lands; of all the land 30% is rainforest, 20% is desert, 10% is ice and 40% is grassland or forest).

The whole planet is surrounded by our **atmosphere**. This mixture of different gases is what enables so many exciting creatures to live on the Earth's surface.

Table 5 Percentage composition of Earth's atmosphere

Gas	Percentage of atmosphere
Nitrogen	78
Oxygen	21
Argon	0.9
Carbon dioxide	0.04
Other	0.06

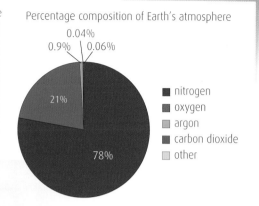

Percentage composition of Earth's atmosphere

 ## Classroom challenge

Selecting information about the Earth's surface

The following questions will help you practise your **selecting skills**. This problem-solving skill enables you to choose information that is relevant to the question. The more you practise your selecting skills, the easier it becomes to find the information you need.

Instructions

Select information from this section to give the correct answer to the following questions.

Questions

1 What is the name given to the mixture of gases that surrounds the planet?
2 What is the average surface temperature on Earth?
3 What percentage of the Earth is covered by desert?
4 What part of the Earth's structure supports life?
5 What fraction of the surface of the Earth is covered in water?
6 What is the name of the seven plates that make up the mantle of the Earth?
7 What is the Earth's core made from?
8 How many miles away from the Sun is the Earth?
9 Name the gases that make up our atmosphere.
10 What type of rock it the mantle made from?

CLIMATE CHANGE

What would happen if the Earth's atmosphere changed? The changing level of carbon dioxide in the atmosphere is a hotly debated subject. For a number of years, scientists have been trying to explain that an increase in carbon dioxide levels in our atmosphere could have dramatic effects on our world.

 Did you know?

The scientific method

Before we look at some quotes from different scientific organisations, it is important to remind ourselves that all scientists work using the 'scientific method'. This means that observations are explained using hypotheses (theories) which can be tested and retested until either accepted or disproven. This is why one single piece of information should never be taken as proof of a fact.

Over time, lots of hypotheses are developed and accepted, building a more complete understanding of a scientific idea. Once this point has been reached, groups of accepted hypotheses can become a 'scientific theory'. A scientific theory is widely accepted by scientists and presents the facts as they are currently understood.

Source 1

'Warming of the climate system is unequivocal, and since the 1950s, many of the observed changes are unprecedented over decades to millennia. The atmosphere and oceans have warmed, the amounts of snow and ice have diminished, and sea level has risen.

Human influence on the climate system is clear, and recent anthropogenic emissions of greenhouse gases are the highest in history. Recent climate changes have had widespread impacts on human and natural systems.'

Source: Intergovernmental Panel on Climate Change (https://www.ipcc.ch/site/assets/uploads/2018/02/AR5_SYR_FINAL_SPM.pdf)

Source 2

'The scientific understanding of climate change is now sufficiently clear to justify taking steps to reduce the amount of greenhouse gases in the atmosphere.' (2005)

Source: U.S. National Academy of Sciences (http://www.aaas.org/sites/default/files/migrate/uploads/1021climate_letter1.pdf)

Source 3

'Observations throughout the world make it clear that climate change is occurring, and rigorous scientific research demonstrates that the greenhouse gases emitted by human activities are the primary driver.' (2009)

Source: American Scientific Societies (Statement on climate change from 18 scientific associations)

Based on this very small sample of quotes released by respected scientific organisations, you can see that scientists now link global warming to 'greenhouse gases', one of which is carbon dioxide.

 Classroom challenge

Researching global warming

Using the information on page 54 and your **researching skills**, answer the following questions.

1 What is the current level of carbon dioxide in the Earth's atmosphere?
2 What is the current average temperature of the Earth?
3 What was the level of carbon dioxide in the atmosphere in August 2007?
4 What was the average temperature of the Earth in August 2007?
5 Name the most common greenhouse gases.
6 What is the main producer of greenhouse gases?
7 What is the greenhouse effect? Draw a diagram to help explain.
8 What is global warming?
9 Are the greenhouse effect and global warming linked?
10 Based on your research and the comments made by the scientific community, write 80–100 words explaining why you think there is (or isn't) a link between carbon dioxide gas and global warming.

THE EARTH'S SURFACE

The crust of the Earth is made up of a huge variety of different kinds of rocks that have been formed through different processes. There are three different types of rocks:

Layers of sedimentary rock

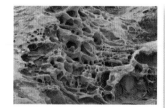
Igneous rock

Vertically tilted metamorphic rock

1 **Sedimentary rocks** are formed from sand, small pebbles and other fragmented materials that have been compressed together in layers over a very long period of time. These rocks are normally relatively brittle and soft, and can break apart very easily. Examples of sedimentary rocks include limestone and sandstone.

Detailed view of limestone

2 **Igneous rocks** are formed when molten magma cools and hardens. Magma comes from deep underground where the temperature is very high. Occasionally, magma erupts onto the Earth's surface and cools into a hard rock. Examples of igneous rock include obsidian and granite.

Detailed view of granite

3 **Metamorphic rocks** are formed underground where rocks are subjected to high temperature and pressure. The squeezing and melting results in a rock that has layers or large crystals. Examples of metamorphic rocks include marble and slate.

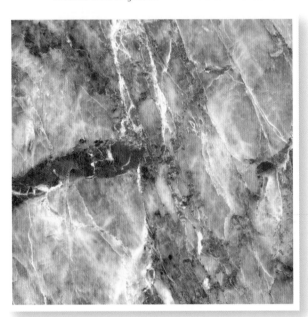

Detailed view of marble

 Classroom challenge

Classifying rocks

Instructions

Table 6 gives a selection of information about a number of different types of rocks. Using this information and the knowledge you have gained from reading this section of the book, answer questions 1–4.

Then, in question 5, use your **analysing** skills to match the stones in the pictures to their names and uses.

Table 6 Types of rocks and their uses

Type of rock	Common uses
Coal	Burned to produce electricity
Limestone	Used in the manufacture of Portland cement, lime, paper, petrochemicals, insecticides, linoleum, fibreglass, glass, carpet backing and as the coating on many types of chewing gum
Shale	A component of bricks and cement
Conglomerate	Used in the construction industry
Sandstone	Used principally for construction, red–brown sandstone which formed in the Triassic age (better known as brownstone) is seen in cities in the east of Scotland
Granite	Used for architectural construction, ornamental stone and monuments
Pumice	Used as an abrasive material in hand soaps and emery boards, for example
Gabbro	Used as crushed stone for concrete aggregate, road metal and railroad ballast for example
	Smaller quantities are cut and polished to be used as decorative dimension stones (called black granite)
Basalt	Used in aggregate
Schist	Used as building stones
Gneiss	Used as building stones and other structural purposes
Quartzite	Has the same uses as sandstone
Marble	Used as dimension stone for statuary (making statues), architectural and ornamental purposes

Questions

1 Which two types of rocks are used for the same purposes? Why do you think this is?
2 What properties does marble have that mean it is good for making statues and ornaments?
3 Which stone is used to coat chewing gum?
4 Which stone do you think is the softest rock? Why?

5 Classify each of the rocks in the photographs as sedimentary, metamorphic or igneous. You must include the reasons for your classifications in your answer.

 How does that work?

The rock cycle

Rocks are recycled and changed, but never made from scratch. This process is known as the **rock cycle**.

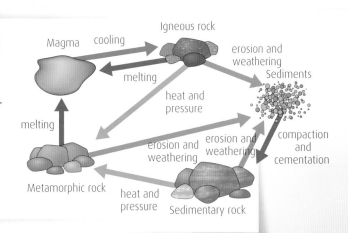

57

Classroom challenge

 **TEACHING NOTES**

Rock cycle experiment

Aim: To see how the rock cycle works

Equipment

- Fruit chew or similar chewy sweet
- Bunsen burner
- Heatproof mat
- Tripod
- Crucible

Instructions

1. Unwrap three sweets and observe their shape, colour and consistency.
2. Add pressure to form 'sedimentary rocks'. This can be done by hand – squash the three sweets together between your fingers or palms. The layers in the sweet rock are like those in sedimentary rocks.
3. Record observations of your sweet sedimentary rocks.
4. Add heat to create 'igneous rocks'. The squashed sweets should be placed in a crucible, on a tripod, above a Bunsen burner. The sweets should be heated until warm but not melted.
5. Record observations of your sweet igneous rocks.
6. Add extreme heat to produce 'metamorphic rocks'. Heat the crucible over a flame until the sweets are melted. Allow to cool before moving.
7. Once cooled, record observations of your sweet metamorphic rocks.

Safety!

Do not eat the sweets.

Heated sweets can cause burns! Do not move the crucible until the sweets have cooled and are no longer molten.

A risk assessment to accompany this experiment can be downloaded from www.brightredpublishing. co.uk

Soil

As you have seen, there are lots of different types of rocks, some of which are useful to us. But the Earth also provides us with other resources. We use the soil and minerals that are found on the Earth's surface too. Soil is formed by the weathering of rocks and minerals and by the addition of organic materials from living things. Air and water are also part of soil.

Soil forms the top layer of the Earth's crust. There are different types of soil, each with its own properties and uses, as shown in Table 7.

Find an extra activity on types of soil in at Homework Helpers bundle at www.brightredpublishing.co.uk

Table 7 Soil types, properties and uses

Type of soil	Properties	Uses
Sand	Large particles Large spaces between particles, giving good water drainage	Aggregate for concrete Foundations for building work Fast draining soil for farming
Loam	Mixture of large and small particles Mixture of different sized spaces between particles, giving variable drainage High in nutrients	Gardening and farming Can be used for rough building when mixed with straw
Clay	Small Small spaces between particles, resulting in poor water drainage	Baked into bricks for building Making ceramics Added to cosmetics (like toothpaste and facemasks)

 ## Classroom challenge

Concrete advice

Minerals are also found on the Earth's surface. They are vital to plants and animals, and we also use them for a variety of different purposes.

Instructions

Using your **researching skills** and the internet or your library resources, find out about two different minerals:

1 quartz
2 gypsum

Write a letter to a local construction company or record a video report in which you explain whether quartz or gypsum is better to use in concrete mixture and why.

Explain the advantages and disadvantages of both minerals, including references to their structure and how they are formed.

Swap your letter or video report with another member of your class. Check each other's work and identify any mistakes.

Metal extraction

As rocks, soils and minerals are formed and recycled, different **compounds** build up. These compounds, called **ores**, are useful to us.

Haematite

One such ore is haematite, which contains iron. Iron is a metal that is used in lots of different industries and it is used to make items that are part of our everyday lives.

Different examples of iron in use

How does that work?

Blast furnace

Iron is removed from iron ore using heat and carbon at a temperature of between 900 and 1300 °C. A **blast furnace** provides a safe way to reach such a high temperature.

The extraction of iron has been carried out since early human history, so we have been refining this process for hundreds of years. The discovery that people could extract and use the metals found in ores has allowed a complex, industrial society to develop.

Remains of an axe from the iron age

Table 8 Metals and their uses

Metal	Uses	Reason for choice
Aluminium	Drink cans	Low density, non-toxic, relatively cheap
	Aircraft parts	Resists corrosion, strong
Copper	Electrical wires	Ductile, good electrical conductor
	Water pipes	Strong, malleable, resists corrosion
Gold	Jewellery	Shiny, attractive, very malleable
	Electronics	Good conductor, resists corrosion
Titanium	Supersonic aircraft Spacecraft	light but strong, resists corrosion

As Table 8 shows, there are many different uses of metals. Some metals are found naturally in a pure state. However, most metals are found in ores. Different metal ores require different methods of extraction. The simplest method of extraction is to heat the ore and collect the metal as it melts and separates.

Classroom challenge

Researching ores

Instructions

This task tests your **researching skills**.

1 Using the resources you have in your classroom and the internet, choose an ore and do some research into which metal your chosen ore contains.
2 Find out how the metal is extracted from its ore and what the pure metal is used for.
3 Remember you should always cite your sources. You should give the full title and author of any book you use, or the full link to the website you used. You should always make sure your sources are **reliable** so that you know your information is correct.
4 Use the information you have found to produce a poster. Your poster should include scientific diagrams of the extraction process and at least two examples of what the metal is used for.

What's the ore?

Instructions

This task requires you to use both your **researching skills** and your **literacy skills**. Look at the list of ore names that have been muddled up. Use the internet to help you unscramble the anagrams and find out about each of the ores.

Questions

For each ore answer these questions.

1 What metal does each ore contain?
2 How is the metal extracted from the ore?
3 What is the metal used for once it has been extracted?

- Tieeirstsca
- Hoietmrc
- Bolceimut
- Matiehet
- Nemletil
- Etitganem
- Luoyrtieps

 **Did you know?**

Characteristics of metals

The Periodic Table can be divided to show metals at one end and non-metals at the other.

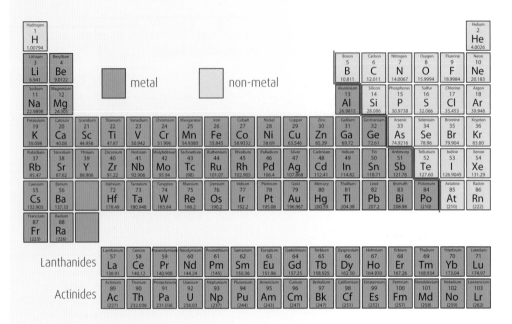

All the metals show similar properties:

- lustrous (shiny)
- malleable (bendy)
- ductile (can be pulled out into wires)
- conductors of electricity and heat
- dense
- strong

All of the elements on the left of the red 'staircase' line are metals; they all have the basic properties. On the other side of the line we find the non-metals; they do not have the same characteristics as metals. The properties of metals mean that many of them are useful to us, so we mine their ores and extract the pure element.

For an additional activity on metal extraction, download the Homework Helpers bundle at www.brightredpublishing.co.uk

When we extract metals from ores we are breaking down compounds to form more useful products. Plants can also provide us with a number of different very useful products when they are broken down and processed. One of the most obvious uses of plants is as food, both for humans and other animals. Plants can also be used as fuel when burned. In the past and present, plants have been and are used as medicines, dyes, perfumes and pesticides (see page 84).

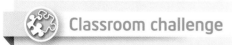

Classroom challenge

Experiment to make a dye

Aim: To demonstrate that plants can make useful products

TEACHING NOTES

Find teaching notes for this challenge at www. brightredpublishing.co.uk

Equipment

- Beakers
- Measuring cylinder
- Glass rods
- Tongs
- Bunsen burners, tripods, gauzes
- Filter funnels with filter paper
- Stands, bosses, clamps
- White fabric
- Beetroot
- Red onion

Instructions

1 Label two beakers: 'Beetroot' and 'Onion'.
2 Add the correct vegetable to each beaker.
3 Add 100 cm³ of water to each beaker.
4 Using a Bunsen burner, boil the vegetable and water for 15 minutes.
5 Allow the beaker to cool for a few minutes.
6 Filter the cooled liquid into clean beakers.
7 Using tongs, add your cotton to the dye bath and boil for 10 minutes, stirring regularly with a glass rod.
8 Remove the material using tongs and allow to dry.
9 Record observations of differences between the dyed fabrics.

Safety!

Take care when boiling water with a Bunsen burner and allow glassware to cool before handling.

Questions

1 Which dye worked the best?
2 Using your **researching skills**, use the internet to find out what other plant materials can be used as dyes.
3 Write up the results of your research and experiment using 80–100 words.

The asteroid continued on its way. Its path was shaped by the different planets it passed on its way. As it hurtled towards the Sun, the possibility of it making contact with our planet increased. But there was still a chance the Earth would escape unscathed.

THE EARTH'S DAYS, YEARS AND SEASONS

This wonderful sphere that we live on is constantly moving, just like the other planets we have looked at. The Earth moves around the Sun in an **orbit**. One cycle around the Sun is what we know as a **year**.

There are four distinct **seasons** in the Earth's year: winter, spring, summer and autumn. The winter here in Scotland runs roughly from December to February, but in Australia these months are summer months. The four seasons have a different weather patterns. We get our warmth and light from our Sun. The difference in temperature during the different seasons is due to the position of the Earth in relation to the Sun. As the tilted Earth orbits around the Sun, different parts of the planet are closer to the Sun (and experience summer) and different parts are farther away (having winter).

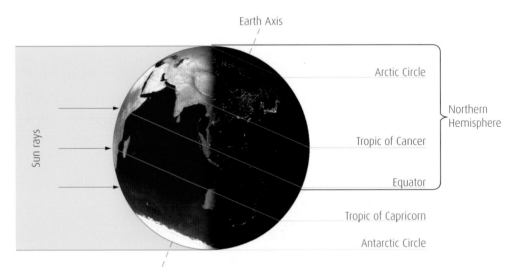

Earth has a North Pole and a South Pole, but it doesn't sit with these pointing straight up and down; the Earth has a tilt (the North Pole points 23.4° away from vertical)

When the North Pole is tilted away from the Sun, countries in the northern hemisphere like Scotland don't get as much warmth and light, so our days are shorter and the temperature is colder. As the Earth moves around the Sun, the tilt means that the northern hemisphere points towards the Sun for the summer months of the year. Our days become lighter and longer, and the temperature becomes warmer. This also explains why, when we have winter, Australia experiences summer; because the South Pole points the opposite way to the North Pole, Australians always have the opposite season to us.

This orbit around the Sun isn't the only movement the Earth makes. The Earth also spins about its axis. The Earth spins at about 1000 miles per hour.

This spinning movement causes us to have days – one spin is one day. We know one orbit around the Sun takes one year; one year is made up of 365.25 days.

How does that work?

The leap year

Every four years, February has an 'extra' day. Our Earth year is made up of 365.25 days, not a round 365 days.

$$0.25 = \frac{1}{4}$$

$$4 \times \frac{1}{4} = 1$$

So, every four years we add one full day to make up for the four quarter days we miss the rest of the time! Years with 366 days are called leap years.

We experience day time when the Sun is lighting the sky – when our part of the world is facing the Sun. Night time is when our part of the Earth is facing away from the Sun, giving us darkness. Each spin on the Earth's axis takes 24 hours to complete, which is why our day is 24 hours long and why our clocks run on a 24-hour cycle.

In the same way that the different sides of the planet experience the seasons at different times of the year, time varies all across the planet. It would be impossible to organise our lives if all places had slightly different times, so we use **time zones**. In Scotland, our time zone is called **Greenwich Mean Time (GMT)** and all other time zones around to world are based on our midnight. When it is noon in Edinburgh it is midnight in Auckland.

 Did you know?

Time zones didn't always exist, Humans made them up! They were proposed by a scientist who was born in Scotland, Sir Sandford Fleming. He proposed the idea of a twenty-four-hour clock and later clarified that the clock should begin at the Anti Meridian of Greenwich. Sir Fleming's original idea has been adapted slightly to be more convenient which is why some countries, such as Turkey, have the same time difference from Greenwich Mean Time (the start of the clock) even though they should have different times at different parts of the country.

Classroom challenge

Time zones

Instructions

Using the map of European time zones and your **processing skills** answer the following questions.

Questions

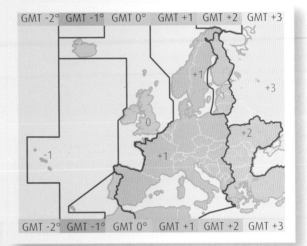

Time zones vary across Europe and round the world in relation to GMT

1 If it is midnight in the United Kingdom, what time would it be in Spain?
2 When it is 2am in the UK, what time would it be in Bulgaria?
3 When it is 5pm in the UK, what time would it be in Iceland?
4 It is 7:30am in the Russian Federation. What time would it be in the UK?
5 Name three countries that have the same time.
6 Name two countries that would have the time of 5:45pm when it is 3:45pm in the UK.
7 What does GMT mean?
8 What time is it in Cyprus when it is 9am in Malta?
9 What time is it in Serbia when it is 1pm in the Netherlands?
10 It is 5pm in Turkey. What time would it be in the UK?

 Classroom challenge

Does Mars have seasons?

Using your library resources or the internet, find out more about the planet Mars and its seasons. Are they like those on Earth? In what ways are they different to Earth's seasons?

The things you should consider when **researching** this question are:

* the distance between the Sun and Mars, compared to the distance between the Sun and Earth
* the length of a year on Mars compared to Earth
* the tilt of Mars compared to Earth.

LIFE ON EARTH

Over the years, scientists have debated what materials and conditions living things require for survival. While there is some disagreement, most scientists agree living things need:

- water
- energy
- shelter.

❝I can sample and identify living things from different habitats to compare their biodiversity and can suggest reasons for their distribution.❞ SCN 3-01a

❝I have collaborated on investigations into the process of photosynthesis and I can demonstrate my understanding of why plants are vital to sustaining life on Earth.❞ SCN 3-02a

❝Through investigations and based on experimental evidence, I can explain the use of different types of chemicals in agriculture and their alternatives and can evaluate their potential impact on the world's food production.❞ SCN 3-03a

❝By contributing to experiments and investigations, I can develop my understanding of models of matter and can apply this to changes of state and the energy involved as they occur in nature.❞ SCN 3-05a

❝I can explain some of the processes which contribute to climate change and discuss the possible impact of atmospheric change on the survival of living things.❞ SCN 3-05b

❝By using my knowledge of our solar system and the basic needs of living things, I can produce a reasoned argument on the likelihood of life existing elsewhere in the universe.❞ SCN 3-06a

❝Through research and discussion, I have contributed to evaluations of media items with regard to scientific content and ethical implications.❞ SCN 3-20b

What's coming up?

- Requirements of life and possibilities of life in the Universe
- Food Chains, sampling and keys
- The process and products of photosynthesis
- Fertilisers
- Climate Change

Our planet is clearly unique. The thing which sets it apart from all of the other planets is that it is teeming with life.

The asteroid was headed for Earth. But what did that mean for life on the planet at that time?

REQUIREMENTS FOR LIFE

Most complex **organisms** require water to survive; humans can only survive three or four days without any water. It is also thought that water was required for life to begin in the first place.

The building blocks of life are able to mix in water and join together to make more complex molecules and compounds. The Earth is the only planet in our Solar System that has pools of water on the surface. Heat from the Sun gives Earth a range of surface temperatures that allows liquid water to exist.

All organisms require energy. The main source of energy in the Solar System is sunlight. The Earth orbits around the Sun at an average distance of 150 000 000 km. This relatively close distance allows sunlight to reach Earth, providing organisms with an energy source.

Organisms require shelter, or an environment that protects them from the many hazards of life. The Earth's atmosphere protects organisms from the inhospitable vacuum of space. The Earth's magnetic field protects organisms from the harmful radiation that is emitted by the Sun and other astronomical objects.

Did you know?
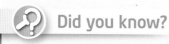

Northern lights

The northern lights or *aurora borealis* are a beautiful display of colours that dance across the night sky at the northernmost parts of the globe. They are usually seen in places such as Iceland and other countries that are close to the North Pole. Sometimes they can be seen from Scotland. There are similar displays across the skies close to the South Pole. These amazing sights are caused by the interaction between the atmosphere of our planet and radiation from the Sun.

The variety of Earth's landscapes and geological features provide shelter for different organisms to aid their survival against harsh conditions.

When we compare these conditions to those found on other planets, we can start to form reasoned arguments about the likelihood of living things existing on other planets.

Classroom challenge

Alien life

Instructions

Using Table 9, which contains information about the different planets, consider the chances of finding life on other planets.

Remember that everyone is entitled to their own opinion. Scientists should always try to base their opinions on fact so you should use all your **problem solving skills here; selecting, processing and analysing.**

Table 9 Comparison of conditions on planets

Planet	Surface	Surface temperature (°C)	Surface gravity (N/Kg)	Atmosphere
Mercury	Rocky	−170 to 420	4	None
Venus	Rocky	460	9	Carbon dioxide
Earth	Rocky	−90 to 60	10	Nitrogen and oxygen
Mars	Rocky	−140 to 35	4	Carbon dioxide
Jupiter	Gas	−110	25	Hydrogen and helium
Saturn	Gas	−140	11	Hydrogen and helium
Uranus	Gas	−200	9	Hydrogen and helium
Neptune	Gas	−200	10	Hydrogen and helium

Use your **literacy skills** to write a letter to a scientific journal expressing your opinion on whether or not there could be life on the other planets in our Solar System. You should include your reasons for thinking a certain way. In your final paragraph, give your opinion about whether there could be life in other parts of space, not just in our Solar System.

Classroom challenge

Is there life beyond our Solar System?

The Solar System is only a very small part of our huge galaxy, the Milky Way. Indeed, our galaxy is quite small compared to the other billions of galaxies in space. A Galaxy is billions of different stars, dust and gases which are held together by an attraction of gravity.

An exoplanet is a planet that orbits a star that is not part of our Solar System. Because there are so many galaxies, there must be countless numbers of exoplanets orbiting the many stars in our Universe. The word Universe is used to represent everything that exists; space as a whole which is thought to be 13 billion years old.

At time of writing, a few thousand exoplanets have been discovered, with hundreds being added every year as our ability to detect these far-off worlds improves.

Instructions

Using your **researching skills** and library resources or the internet, try to find out the names of any exoplanets that scientists believe *may* have the conditions to support life as we know it. Explain why your chosen exoplanets may have the ability to harbour alien life. Make sure you consider the need for water, energy and shelter in your answer.

Visit the Bright Red website and download the Homework Helpers for an extra activity on life in the Universe.

STATES OF MATTER

While water appears to be a very common compound throughout the Solar System, Earth is the only planet where all three matter states of water exist at the same time:

- solid – ice
- liquid – water
- gas – water vapour or steam

All materials are made up from tiny particles. Matter can exist in three different forms depending on the arrangement of these particles:

- **Solids** are materials in which the particles are packed very close together in an ordered pattern. The particles don't move much – they can only vibrate on the spot. As a result, solid objects tend to hold a defined shape and set volume.

- **Liquids** are materials in which the particles, like those in solids, have very little space between them, but there is no defined pattern of arrangement (there is a random arrangement). This means the particles are able to move around. As a result, liquids have no shape and instead take the shape of the container they do have a fixed volume though.

- **Gases**, like liquids, have a random particle arrangement but the spacing between the particles is much greater. The particles can move in all directions very quickly. Gases cannot hold a shape or volume but can be compressed due to the large spaces between the particles.

Classroom challenge

Solids, liquids and gases

Instructions

Using the information on page 70 and your **selecting skills,** answer the following questions about all three types of particle arrangements.

Questions

1 Give an example of one substance that is a solid, one that is a liquid and one that is a gas. Do not include water.
2 Draw a particle arrangement diagram of each of the three states of matter.
3 Describe the properties of each state of matter.
4 Explain how these properties are linked to the particle arrangement in each state.

Instructions

Water exists in a number of different places in the Solar System. Use your **researching skills** to access the internet to find out where water can be found in the Universe.

Make a presentation of your findings.

Remember, as with any research task, you should gather your information from reliable places and cite your sources.

 Did you know?

Titan

Titan, a moon of Saturn, has fascinated scientists for many years. It is the only moon in the Solar System that has an atmosphere. Titan's atmosphere is nothing like ours – it is mainly made of methane gas. However, the world of astronomy exploded with excitement when the Huygens space probe landed on the surface of Titan in January 2005 and discovered that all three states of methane are present: methane gas in the atmosphere, rivers and lakes of liquid methane, and solid methane 'ice'.

Classroom challenge

Marking homework

To really understand a concept, it can be helpful to teach others what you know.

Instructions

Here is a piece of homework that has been submitted for marking. Your job is to be the teacher and give feedback on this work. Use your **analysing skills** to comment on any mistakes, explaining what is wrong. Don't forget to leave positive feedback where it is deserved!

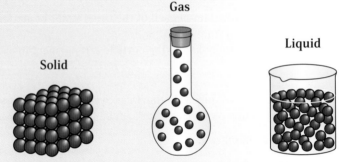

Gas

Solid

Liquid

There are three common states of matter. These states are solid, liquid and gas.

Solids have a fixed volume and a shape that does not change. The particles that make up a solid are packed together and locked into place. Ice is the solid form of water. A solid's volume does not change, but it will take on the shape of its container.

Liquids have a fixed volume but a changeable shape. The atoms and molecules that make up a liquid are loosely held together and not locked into place. Water is a liquid.

The volume and shape of gases change readily. When water evaporates it becomes water vapour, which is a gas.

Head to www.brightredpublishing.co.uk and download the Homework Helpers for additional activities on the states of matter.

DINOSAURS

The asteroid was pulled towards our delicate planet and the life on it was about change forever. The sky burned brightly as the asteroid entered the upper atmosphere. It was travelling so fast and getting so hot that it was brighter even than the Sun.

At impact the entire planet shuddered with the shockwaves that travelled around the globe and through the mantle. There was a huge hole in the crust where the asteroid hit. So much dirt, dust and debris was thrown into the air that the sky went dark.

That one moment in time changed the Earth completely. Some living things on the planet were directly affected by the impact, but others felt the aftereffects for years to come. Entire species died off and new species evolved in the new conditions.

The Earth continued to turn on its axis and to orbit the Sun, as is if nothing at all had happened.

The asteroid impact occurred in the region we now call the Americas. This happened 65.5million years ago, during the Cretaceous period of the Mesozoic era, known as the 'Age of the Dinosaurs'.

The land then didn't look like it does now. There were many active volcanoes, filling the air with ash and smoke pollutants. The level of the ocean was much higher, because the climate was much warmer and the polar ice caps had melted (much as they are doing now because of global warming).

*The plants were different and the animals were unrecognisable compared to the ones in the Americas today. The impact of the asteroid irreparably damaged this delicate **ecosystem**.*

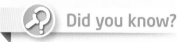 Did you know?

Prehistoric time

The Earth's history can be broken down into different eras. Each era is a span of time that is characterised by the evolution of different forms of life.

During the Paleozoic era the first complex life forms evolved and moved from the ocean to the land. After an extinction event, the Mesozoic era, or the 'Age of the Dinosaurs', began. The dinosaurs, which were the prevalent life forms during the Mesozoic era, started off small and evolved into much larger

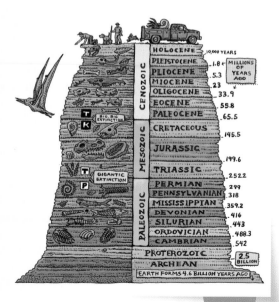

animals. After another big extinction event, the Cenozoic era began and mammals started their evolution. This is the era in which human evolution took place.

The eras were all massively long periods of time, for example the Mesozoic era lasted approximately 180 million years. An era is split into different periods. For example, the Cretaceous period, when dinosaurs grew larger and flowering plants evolved, lasted 79 million years. The extinction event that brought the Cretaceous period to an end is thought to be linked to the formation of the Chicxulub crater in Mexico. The crater is 110 miles across and was probably formed when an asteroid hit the Earth. The effects would have been devastating.

You will be familiar with some of the big names of the Cretaceous era: *Tyrannosaurus rex*, *Triceratops* and *Velociraptor*, for example. You might think that such fierce and hardy creatures wouldn't be affected by an asteroid impact. The truth is that practically every living thing on the planet would have been affected. We refer to this impact now as an **extinction event**. To understand what this means, we need to look closer at the lives of these animals.

Let's take *T. rex* as an example.

FOOD CHAINS AND WEBS

T. rex would have been at the top of its **food chain**. This means that no other animal ate *T. rex* to gain energy. Food chains are a way of showing feeding relationships in an environment. They allow scientists show the flow of energy from one living organism to another.

The arrows in a food chain show which way the energy flows. The grass is known as a **producer** because it makes its own food from the Sun. This happens in a process called **photosynthesis**. Plants take energy from the Sun, carbon dioxide from the air and water from the ground, and convert them into oxygen and sugars.

Animals then eat plants to gain energy from the sugars. The energy transfers from the plants to the animals, which are known as **primary consumers**. An example of a primary consumer today would be a rabbit.

In the Cretaceous period, *Triceratops* was a primary consumer in the *T. rex* food chain. *Triceratops* was easy **prey** for faster **predators** because it was large and slow moving. Predators like *T. rex*, which eat primary consumers, are called **secondary consumers**. Predators that eat secondary consumers are known as tertiary consumers

T-rex (secondary consumer)

Triceratops (primary consumer)

Grass (producer)

Classroom challenge

Food chains

Food chains happen all around us, all the time. You are part of a food chain when you eat a meal.

Word bank

herring	salmon	bear	leaf	caterpillar	bird	snake	turtles	alligator	human
plankton	water snail	tuna	dolphin	squid	seal	orca	bamboo	panda	shrub
giraffe	lion	nuts	squirrels	hawk	dandelions	snail	frog	fox	

Questions

1 Using the word bank and your **processing skills**, construct five different food chains. You may need to **research** to check what the animals normally eat.
2 Grass, leaves and other plants that carry out photosynthesis are known as producers. Where do producers get their energy?
3 Give three examples of secondary consumers in your local area.

As you can imagine, *T. rex* didn't only eat *Triceratops*. Food chains don't show how complicated the feeding relationships between different animals really are. A number of different food chains can be arranged into a **food web**.

A food web is a large, sometimes complicated, diagram of all the different food chains in an **ecosystem**.

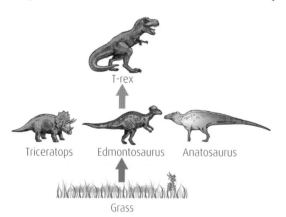

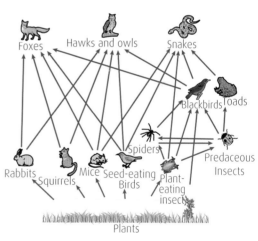

Examples prehistoric and present day food webs

Classroom challenge

Examining food chains and webs

Instructions

A food web includes a number of different food chains. **Process** both of the food webs to answer the following questions.

Questions

1 Identify three different food chains from the food webs.
2 Which animal is at the top of each food web?
3 Name any secondary consumers that are eaten by three other animals.
4 Give an example of a producer from each web.
5 Give an example of a primary consumer from each web.
6 Which animals are secondary consumers?

Food chains in different environments

Instructions

Create an example simple food chain (producer → primary consumer → secondary consumer) for each of the following areas on Earth. You will need to **research** in books or internet resources to ensure the organisms you use in each simple food chain are native to that area.

1 The Amazon rainforest
2 The Pacific Ocean

3 The Arctic Circle
4 The Sahara Desert

Food webs can be very complicated. A change in a food web can cause wide ranging effects for all the other animals. Let's have a look in more detail at what would happen if a change happened in the dinosaur food web (see page 75).

Let's think about what might happen if *T. rex* disappeared completely. Losing a secondary or tertiary consumer like *T. rex* has an impact on the primary consumers of the food web. If fewer primary consumers are eaten, the population will increase. As a result, there will be more competition for food and the producers may be eaten completely. Primary consumers may be more likely to starve, resulting in a decrease in their numbers.

What happens if a primary consumer is removed from a food web? The producer population will increase if there are fewer primary consumers to eat the producers. Fewer primary consumers also means less food for secondary consumers to eat – they will start to starve and numbers will fall.

Removing the producer has an effect all the way up the food chain. With decreased plant life, primary consumers start to die off, leaving less food for secondary consumers and they too experience a decrease in population.

 Classroom challenge

Impact of changes in a food web

As you have seen the effects of losing parts of a food web can be far reaching.

 DON'T FORGET

This activity refers to the more complex modern food web.

Instructions

1. Look at the food web on page 75.
2. Create an informational leaflet about what will happen to the food web when
   (a) a producer, (b) a primary consumer and (c) a secondary consumer is removed.
3. Name the animal or plant populations that would change in each situation.
4. Make sure your leaflets are colourful and eye catching!

For an extra activity on food webs and interdependence, download the Homework Helpers bundle from the Bright Red website!

In the event of the asteroid impact, many dinosaurs were killed and prehistoric food webs would have been affected.

However, it wasn't necessarily this that caused the extinction event. In the aftermath of the impact, the dust and debris in the atmosphere would have prevented sunlight reaching the Earth. The plants, the producers, would have been unable to make food by photosynthesis and all food chains would have collapsed.

SAMPLING AND KEYS

It is difficult for us to know any detail about the food webs that existed during the time of asteroid impact. The main difficulty is that humans were not there to observe the interactions between plants and animals. Using fossils, we can make educated guesses, or hypotheses, about what food the dinosaurs ate, but we will never really know.

Today it is much easier for us to have an understanding of how the Sun's energy flows through food webs. We can make observations of the organisms that live in any given area and how they interact. We find out which organisms live in an environment by taking samples of the **biodiversity**. There are a number of sampling techniques, for example, pitfall traps, pond dipping and quadrats. Using these three techniques, we can look at land animals, aquatic animals and plant life.

Pitfall traps and pond dipping are similar in that organisms are captured and physically removed from their environment in order to be identified and counted.

Quadrats are different as they do not require the plants to be removed from where they grow. The sample in a quadrat is used to calculate the percentage cover of different plants in a wider area. The identification of different species can be quite difficult, so keys are often used.

How does that work?

Which dinosaur?

Keys allow users to identify organisms as accurately as possible. A key consists of a series of questions about an organism's appearance and decision pathways that lead to identification of single species.

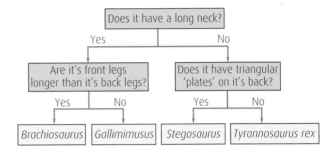

Classroom challenge

Using keys and samples

Instructions

Process the information in the key to answer the questions below.

Dinosaur 1

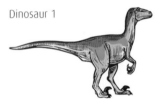

Dinosaur 2

Questions

1. a. What type of dinosaur is dinosaur 1?
   b. What type of dinosaur is dinosaur 2?
2. Which sampling method would be best for figuring out if a field has enough grass to feed a herd of cattle?
3. Which method of sampling would work best to investigate beetle numbers?
4. Using your **researching skills**, find out about three other methods of sampling that you could use to count numbers of different living things.
5. Using the branched key above to guide you, make your own branched key on any topic. Why make a key to identify your sports teams, scientists or music artists?

A key to friendship

Create a key that would help someone identify you and five friends or family members. With permission, take a photo each face and then produce a key that could be used to tell the people apart. Base your key on features like:

- hair colour
- eye colour
- hair style
- nose shape
- presence or absence of freckles
- ears

PHOTOSYNTHESIS

We already know that plants make food using sunlight, water and carbon dioxide in a process called photosynthesis. Photosynthesis is an incredibly important chemical reaction – without it all plants and the animals that feed on them would die.

Here is the equation for photosynthesis:

carbon dioxide + water $\longrightarrow$ glucose + oxygen

$$6CO_2 + 6H_2O \longrightarrow C_6H_{12}O_6 + 6O_2$$

The purpose of photosynthesis is to allow plants to produce their own food; sugar.

Carbon dioxide in the atmosphere is absorbed by the leaves of the plant, while water from the soil is absorbed by the roots of the plant. With the help of sunlight, these two chemicals combine to form glucose (sugar) and oxygen. Glucose is used as food for the plant and oxygen is released into the atmosphere as a by-product. We can test for both products of this reaction in the lab.

How does that work?

Photosynthesis experiment

Aim: To demonstrate that oxygen is produced by photosynthesis

Equipment

- Beaker
- Water
- Test tube
- Funnel
- Aquatic plant

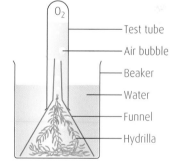

Instructions

1. Fill the beaker with water.
2. Prepare an aquatic plant, such as Hydrilla. Cut the stems of the plants and tie them with a thread. Place the stems upside down in the beaker of water and cover them with an inverted funnel so that the cut ends are towards the neck of the funnel.
3. Fill a test tube with water and invert it over the neck of the funnel.
4. Keep the whole apparatus in sunlight and observe over time.
5. The gas that collects pushes water out of the test tube, creating a large bubble that can be tested to demonstrate it is oxygen. When the gas bubble is large enough, the test tube can be removed from the set-up and the gas tested with a glowing splint. If the splint relights and a flame appears, this demonstrates that the gas made by the plant is oxygen.

How does that work?

Investigation into sugar (starch) production by plants

Aim: To test for the presence of starch in a leaf

Testing for glucose is more difficult than testing for oxygen, because the glucose that is made during the reaction is converted to starch for storage. The presence of starch indicates that the plant made glucose during the photosynthesis reaction

Equipment

- Leaves
- 250 cm³ beaker
- Tweezers
- Glass rod
- Boiling tube
- Petri dish
- White tile
- Ethanol
- Hot water
- Iodine solution

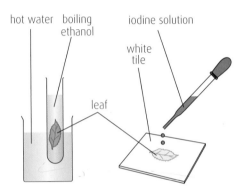

Instructions

1 Place a leaf in a beaker of hot water and leave for 1 minute.
2 Remove the hot leaf with tweezers and place it into boiling tube.
3 Cover the leaf with ethanol and place the boiling tube in a beaker of freshly boiled water.
4 Agitate the leaf with the tweezers and observe as the leaf start to lose its colour.
5 Once the leaf is colourless, remove it from the ethanol with tweezers and rinse it with cold water.
6 Place the leaf on the Petri dish, which is itself placed on top of the white tile.
7 Add a couple of drops of iodine to the leaf and observe. If a blue–black colour is visible then starch is present.

Safety!

Ethanol is highly flammable. Never use an open flame in the vicinity of ethanol. In this experiment we use a kettle for boiling water rather than a Bunsen burner to reduce this risk

Iodine solution can stain the skin or clothing if spilled.

 **TEACHING NOTES**

Find teaching notes for this investigation at www.brightredpublishing. co.uk

Classroom challenge

 **TEACHING NOTES**

Find teaching notes
for this challenge at
www.brightredpublishing.
co.uk

Design an experiment to investigate the rate of photosynthesis

Instructions

1 Design an experiment to test a factor that affects the rate of photosynthesis.
2 What factor could you change to see if it affects photosynthesis?
3 How would you measure how much photosynthesis is taking place?
4 What equipment would you need?
5 Write down an example of a table you could use to collect results.

You can find an extra activity on photosynthesis in our Homework Helpers. Just head to the Bright Red website and download them for free.

GROWING HEALTHY PLANTS

As we know plants produce their own food by photosynthesis, but they also require certain **minerals** to grow properly. There are three main chemical elements that plants require to grow well – nitrogen, potassium and phosphorus. If these minerals are absent, plants do not survive. We can help plant producers to survive and grow well using fertilisers, even if the soil lacks minerals.

This plant needs more Nitrogen to grow and would require a fertiliser with a NPK value of 10:5:5

This plant needs more Phosphorus to grow and requires a fertiliser with an NPK value of 0:24:16

This plant needs more Potassium to grow and requires a fertiliser with an NPK value of 16:16:24

Fertilisers are water-soluble chemicals that add Nitrogen (chemical symbol N), Phosphorus (chemical symbol P) and Potassium (chemical symbol K) to the soil. Plants grown with fertilisers usually grow greener, larger and more quickly than those without. Each different type of fertiliser has a specific mixture of the different elements, known as its NPK value (with NPK standing for Nitrogen, Phosphorus and Potassium). The NPK value is usually found on the fertiliser label.

Comparison between fertilised and unfertilised plants

How does that work?

Fertiliser experiment

Aim: To make nitrogen-rich fertiliser (ammonium sulfate)

Equipment

- Evaporating basin
- Gauze
- Tripod
- Bunsen burner
- 20 cm^3 measuring cylinder
- Filter paper
- Filter funnel
- Conical flask (to stand funnel on)
- Glass rod
- Sulfuric acid 1 mol dm^{-1}
- Ammonia solution 2 mol
- Full-range indicator paper

Find teaching notes for this experiment at
www.brightredpublishing.co.uk

Instructions

1   Put 20 ml sulfuric acid into an evaporating basin.
2   Add the ammonia solution a little at a time, with stirring, until a definite smell of ammonia is obtained.
3   Check the pH is 7 or above with indicator paper.
4   Evaporate the solution to about one-fifth of its original volume. **Take care** – do not let the solution spit. Cool the concentrated solution.
5   Filter off the crystals and dry them.
6   Once the crystals are dry, they can be mixed with water and used to feed plants.

Safety!

Wear eye protection throughout the experiment.

Ammonia solution gives off ammonia which can irritate the eyes and respiratory system.

Sulfuric acid can cause chemical burns, so take care to not get it on the skin.

 Classroom challenge

Can you create your own fertiliser?

Instructions

Gro-Green Fertiliser 20:5:10

1   Choose one of the mineral-deficient plants from the photos on page 81.
2   Design a fertiliser that could be used to treat the plant you have chosen. You will need to consider what nutrients the fertiliser needs to contain to make your plant grow bigger and stronger.

3 Design the packaging for your fertiliser. Your labelling should tell the purchaser the brand name, chemical ingredients, benefits and price. Your design should be eye catching and not misleading! Don't forget to include the ingredients table.

Visit www.brightredpublishing.co.uk and download our Homework Helpers bundle for an additional activity on fertilisers.

If fertilisers are so good at helping plants grow fast and stronger, why don't we use them for all plants?

There are pollution problems associated with fertilisers. Because they are water soluble, any chemical that is not taken up by a plant can enter the **water cycle**.

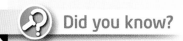
Did you know?

Water cycle

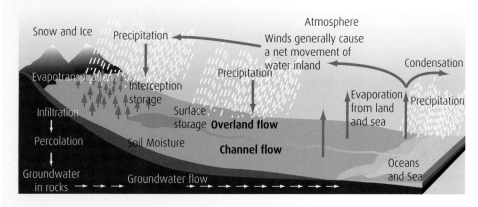

As with the rock cycle, the chemicals on the Earth cannot just appear. They must be here to start with and they don't just disappear, even if we can't see. The water that is critical to life on Earth is constantly recycling.

When looking at the water cycle diagram we can start at any point, but let's start at the top. Clouds form in the air due to the cooler temperature at a distance from the surface of the Earth. Water vapour particles in the air condense into clouds as the temperature decreases. Droplets in clouds gather together and precipitate as rain or snow. Water from rain or snow collects in the waterways or sinks into the ground. Water in rivers, lakes and oceans is then heated by the Sun and turned back into vapour. This starts to condense and turn into clouds and the whole process starts again.

How does that work?

Try it yourself. Take a freezer bag and fill it one-third full with water. Seal the bag with the remaining two-thirds full of air. Attach the sealed bag to a window that gets direct sunlight and then wait. You will start to see all the stages of the water cycle in your own bag!

Fertilisers dissolve in water, which means that they can be washed into places where they are not needed causing damage. Sometimes fertilisers get washed into lakes and rivers. Algae is an aquatic plant that grows faster when fertiliser is present. When the algae population in a lake grows bigger and quicker than normal, it can use up the oxygen in the water and block sunlight, causing fish and other aquatic life to die. We have already looked at how bad it can be to lose part of a food web. This is why the use of fertilisers should be restricted as much as possible.

Download our Homework Helpers for an additional activity on nutrients for healthy plants and to use your **researching skills**.

There are other methods that farmers can use to make sure crops are produced as fast as possible and in quantity:

- **Pesticides** are chemicals that are used to ensure crops are protected against pests such as fungi, insects, rodents and other competing plants. Pesticides kill pests.
- **Herbicides** are a type of pesticide. They are chemicals that can be used to clear areas of land of weeds without damaging the crops. Once the land has been cleared, it can be **cultivated** as productive farmland.

Not all methods of boosting crop growth and preventing damage by pests use chemicals. There are some **organic** or **natural** methods. These have the same results as chemical fertilisers and pesticides but are thought to have less impact on the environment.

- Natural fertilisers are usually waste products, like manure, that contain the minerals that plants need to grow in a form that they can absorb.
- Natural pesticides tend to be made from plant oils and extracts which are not harmful to the environment.
- In companion planting the gardener plants different types of plants together. Some companion plants are used to lure pests away from ones the gardener is trying to protect and others are strongly scented to deter pests.

There are positives and negatives to both synthetic (made by people) and natural fertilisers and pesticides.

 ## Classroom challenge

Synthetic versus natural debate

Instructions

1   It's time to use your **researching skills** and **processing skills** again. You should use the resources in your classroom and the internet to look at the pros and cons of synthetic versus natural fertilisers and/or pesticides.
2   Present your findings in the form of a debate.

3   Work with a partner – take one side of
    the argument each.
4   Write your argument for why natural or synthetic
    fertilisers and pesticides are the better option.
5   Be prepared to share it!

The glyphosate controversy

Instructions

There is currently a scientific and political argument over one of the most heavily used
herbicides in the world: glyphosate. Using the internet, **research** the topic to answer the
following questions.

Questions

1   Why do many people think the use of glyphosate a big problem?
2   What impact do you think banning this substance will have on agriculture?
3   What is your opinion? Should glyphosate be banned? Give reasons for your answer.

CLIMATE CHANGE

*Our planet has been changing continuously since the asteroid impact and
dinosaur extinction that set the course for human evolution. Humans have
been influencing the planet since their evolution, more so since the Industrial
Revolution which began in the eighteenth century.*

*Scientific and technological development always has advantages and drawbacks.
Every leap forwards that human society makes could influence the future of the
planet. One specific example of human influence on the planet is climate change.*

As we have developed our ability to use the Earth's resources to satisfy our needs, we
have contributed to a problem called the **greenhouse effect**.

We rely on the Sun for warmth and light, both of which are vital to the balance of life on
Earth. Our **atmosphere** allows some **solar radiation** to reach the Earth's surface, where
is causes heating, and some radiation is reflected back into space.

Water vapour, carbon
dioxide, nitrous oxide,
ozone and methane are
examples of greenhouse
gases. These gases
naturally trap the heat
that the Sun provides
during the day and stops
it all from escaping
during the night. This
is how the planet stays

Some enrgy is
reflected back
out into space

Earth's surface is heated by
the Sun and radiates the heat
back out towards space

The greenhouse effect

Greenhouse gases in the
atmosphere trap some of the heat

Solar energy
from the Sun
passes through
the atmosphere

at a life-sustaining average temperature of 15°C. However, when the levels of greenhouse gases in the atmosphere rise, too much heat is trapped overnight. This causes the average temperature of the Earth to rise. If the temperature changes too much, weather patterns alter causing **climate change**.

A major contributor to the increase in greenhouse gases is human technology. The **Industrial Revolution** increased the concentration of carbon dioxide in the atmosphere. This is because people discovered that burning fossil fuels (coal, oil, natural gas and peat) can power machinery and keep us warm.

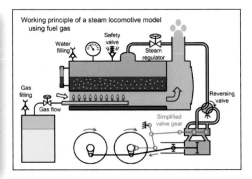

Working principle of a steam locomotive model using fuel gas

 Classroom challenge

Design your own machine!

Instructions

Invent your own steam-powered machine.

Get creative! Your invention can have any function you like. You are only limited by your imagination.

In your notes, draw a diagram of your invention, explaining its job and how it works.

It is not just our use of fossil fuels that has increased the concentration of carbon dioxide in the atmosphere. Humans have impacted the planet in other ways too.

Deforestation is a problem we have caused. In order to make more space to live, to farm animals to eat and have enough space to grow foods, we had to find land.

Think back to the start of the chapter when we looked at the different habitats on Earth. There are rainforests, deserts, grasslands, forests and the ice continents. Obviously, some of these environments wouldn't work for our uses – you can't breed cows or grow corn on Antarctica.

The areas we could develop into usable land were limited. We could only take land that we know would sustain life, so chose to take from the forests and rainforests. So many forests have been destroyed that greenhouse gases have been affected.

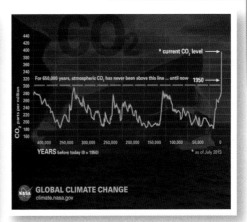

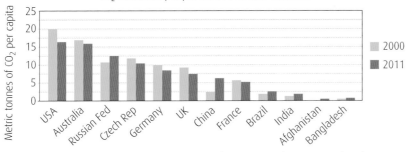

Who emits most carbon dioxide?
CO_2 emissions per person for selected countries

Source: United Nations Statistics Division Milennium Development Goals Indicators,
2011 figures, database last updated July 6, 2015.

As you know, plants use carbon dioxide in photosynthesis to produce their own food. They take the carbon dioxide out of the atmosphere and replace it with oxygen. Humans have removed so many trees and plants that the delicate balance of gases in the atmosphere has been destroyed. Carbon dioxide is not being removed from the air quickly enough because there are simply not enough trees.

 Classroom challenge

Carbon dioxide is a greenhouse gas

Instructions

Using your **processing skills**, examine the graphs and answer the following questions.

Questions

1 For how many years was the CO_2 level in the atmosphere below 300 ppm?
2 Approximately how much CO_2 is in the atmosphere now?
3 Approximately how low has the CO_2 level been in the past?
4 Which country emitted the most CO_2 in 2000?

5 Which country emitted the least?
6 Name three countries that have decreased their CO_2 output since 2000.
7 Which countries have increased their CO_2 output?
8 Why might those countries have increased the volume of CO_2 they produce?
9 How could these countries could start to decrease their output over the next 10 years?

 ### Classroom challenge

The Paris Agreement

On 4 November 2016, the Paris Agreement came into effect. It was a treaty signed by nearly 200 representatives of countries from around the world.

Instructions

Using your **researching skills** and library resources or the internet, find out what issue the Paris Agreement is attempting to tackle and how it will try to do that.

Questions

1 What is the Paris Agreement?
2 When was it signed and by whom?
3 How will signatories of the Paris Agreement tackle climate change?

Download our Homework Helpers bundle for an extra activity on climate change.

RENEWABLE ENERGY

It is hard to see how we can continue to make scientific and technological advancements without causing more damage to our planet. However, we are now at a point where we understand some of the things we have done wrong in the past. Humans are trying to use our combined intellect to build solutions to the problems we have created and to develop society in a sustainable way.

Burning fossil fuels has not only caused climate change, but it has also been using up our fuel resources. Fossil fuels are a **finite resource** – they will eventually run out. If we continue using oil in the way we currently do, a shortage will occur in your lifetime. Scotland as a country has acknowledged this issue and has invested research effort and finance in the development of **renewable energies**.

Most Scots are aware of renewable energy technologies as many of us live near a windfarm.

Massive wind turbines have propellers that are designed to move with the wind. The propellers turn a rotor which is connected to a generator which creates electricity for the National Grid. The Grid supplies electricity for homes and industry.

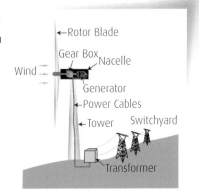

As Scotland is naturally a windy place, our windfarms supply a fairly constant source of power. Some other methods of renewable energy are not as reliable in our country.

 Classroom challenge

Wind power

Instructions

Choose one of the large windfarms in Scotland. Find out all about it by answering these questions.

1 Where is the wind farm located?
2 Why was that location a good site for a wind farm?
3 How much electricity does it generate in a year?
4 Why it is important for us to continue to grow this type of infrastructure?
5 Present your information as an advert for wind power; you can use a poster, video or radio advert format.

Solar panels, hydropower, geothermal power and wind turbines all work on a similar principle. They use natural resources that will not run out to produce electricity.

Renewable Technology	Power produced from	Advantages	Disadvantages
Solar Panels	Sunlight	· Sunlight is free. · Can be placed on existing buildings or open land. · Save on utility bills.	· Expensive to install. · Sunlight only available during daytime. · Only 22% of light captured is converted to energy. · Location (Scotland has short, dark days for large parts of the year).
Hydropower	Water	· Reliable, changes to electrical output are easily controlled. · Hydropower is a non-polluting form of energy.	· Can cause environmental problems for aquatic life. · Building the Hydroelectric plant is expensive. · Droughts can cause issues with electrical output.
Geothermal Power	Heat of the Earth	· Reliable, highly efficient form of power. · Very little maintenance required.	· Highest upfront costs of all the renewable sources. · Geothermal sites can cool down over time. · System requires land to be installed on.
Wind Turbines	Wind	· Wind energy is free. · Can be large, industrial systems or small individual systems. · Low maintenance and running costs.	· Installation is expensive and could be considered ugly. · The wind fluctuates so energy output isn't easy to control. · Wind turbines are loud and can be heard from meters away. · Can be a threat to wildlife such as birds and bats.

These methods of power generation will continue to be a viable resource once oil runs out. These technologies will develop further to become more reliable and efficient, and easier to use.

What next?

HOLOCENE	10,000 YEARS
PLEISTOCENE	1.8
PLIOCENE	5.3
MIOCENE	23
OLIGOCENE	33.9
EOCENE	55.8
PALEOCENE	65.5
CRETACEOUS	145.5

MILLIONS OF YEARS AGO

We know quite a lot about how the impact of the asteroid affected the Earth. How have we changed the world since the start of human evolution?

Think of the difference between the food webs for T. Rex and modern food webs. Humans are at the top of many food chains. This shows how we have changed the world to suit our needs.

The Earth's human population is growing, placing increasing demands on land for space to live and grow food and producing more greenhouse gases. What can we do to ensure that climate change doesn't have a devastating impact, but at the same time meet our food and land needs?

It's young people that will discover the answers to these questions. You are the scientists of the future. So, I ask you: What is next? Are we headed towards another extinction event or a bright future?

Problem-solving skills developed

I can:

- researching a topic to collect, edit sort and present findings in a variety of different mediums
- select information from tables and passages
- process information to form valid conclusions
- analyse information to form valid conclusions
- draw a bar graph, with headings, axis labels and appropriate scale with units, using data displayed in a table
- use a bar graph to select information to answer questions
- draw a line graph, with headings, axis labels and an appropriate scale, using data displayed in a table
- use a line graph to select information
- make predictions using the patterns found in an incomplete set of data
- use an equation to process data and give an answer, with appropriate units
- analyse a set of data from a graph, chart or table to describe a relationship or a pattern
- plan an experiment that describes changing a factor (independent variable) to see its effect on another variable (dependant variable)
- write a report on an experiment that includes a title, aim, method, list of apparatus, results, conclusion and evaluation.

 **What you now know**

The Solar System
- A planet is an object that orbits a star.
- A moon is an object that orbits a planet.
- A star is a huge sphere of gas that radiates light and heat.
- An asteroid is a rock that is moving through space. Billions of asteroids orbit the Sun in the asteroid belt.
- The Oort cloud is an orbit of icy rocks at the outer edge of the Solar System.
- The Solar System consists of the Sun and its orbiting planets and moons.

Days and years
- A year is the time it takes for a planet to orbit around the Sun once.
- A day is the time that it takes for a planet to rotate once on its own axis.

Gravity
- Gravity is an attractive force between masses.
- The weight of an object is the force a mass experiences due to gravity (weight is measured in newton, N).
- The mass of an object is a measure of how the matter in an object (mass is measured in kilograms, kg).
- Gravitational field strength is a measure of the strength of the gravitational pull a planet has on masses at its surface (this measured in newton per kilogram, N/kg).
- weight = mass × gravitational field strength
- Different planets and moons have different gravitational field strengths.
- The gravitational field strength decreases as the distance from the surface of a planet increases.

Structure of the Earth
- The Earth's interior is made of three main layers: the core, the mantle and the crust.
- The core is at the centre of the planet and is made from molten iron.
- The mantle is made of mainly silicate rock.
- The crust, the thin outermost layer, is made of rock and forms the Earth's surface.
- The atmosphere is a thin layer of a mixture of gases (mainly nitrogen and oxygen) that surrounds the surface of the Earth.

Rocks
- There are three different kinds of rocks that make up our crust: igneous, sedimentary and metamorphic.
- Igneous rocks are formed from cooled molten magma that has erupted from deep underground.
- Sedimentary rocks are formed from layers of sand and pebbles that are compacted together underground.
- Metamorphic rocks have been subjected to very high temperatures and pressures underground.
- There are different types of soil that have different properties and characteristics, which means they are suited to different jobs.
- Quartz and gypsum are examples of minerals.

Metal extraction

- Ores are compounds that contain metals.
- Metals can be separated from the rest of the compounds in the ore by heating to a very high temperature.

Life on Earth
- Living things, organisms, require energy, water and shelter.
- Water is required to sustain living things, as well as to provide an environment for the building blocks of organic compounds to mix together.
- Energy is required to allow organisms to function and grow.
- Shelter is required to protect organisms from harmful conditions.

States of matter
- There are three states of matter: solid, liquid and gas.
- Solids have particles that are held closely together and are arranged in an ordered pattern.
- Liquids have particles that are held closely together but can move around in a disordered pattern.
- Gases have particles that are much further apart and move in a disordered pattern.

Food chains and webs
- A producer is a food-making organism in a food chain.
- A primary consumer is an organism that eats a producer to gain the energy in food.
- A secondary consumer eats prey (a primary consumer) for energy.
- A food chain shows the flow of energy from producers, through primary consumers, to secondary consumers.
- A food web shows the complex connections between a number of food chains.
- Biodiversity is a measure of the variety of organisms that are located in an area.
- A key can be used to identify species of organisms.

Photosynthesis
- Photosynthesis is the process used by plants to make food for energy.
- Carbon dioxide + Water → Glucose + Oxygen.
- Sunlight is required for this chemical reaction to take place.

Fertilisers and herbicides
- Fertilisers are a mixture of chemicals that provide plants with the nutrient minerals they require to grow.
- Fertilisers contain Nitrogen, Phosphorus and Potassium – chemicals required for healthy plant growth.
- Herbicides are chemical mixtures that kill plants.

Climate change
- Climate change is the long-term change in the Earth's climatic conditions.
- Climate change is mainly caused by the build-up of carbon dioxide in our atmosphere.
- Industry, transportation and deforestation are thought to be the main contributors to carbon dioxide increase in our atmosphere.
- Renewable energy sources provide methods of producing energy that do not release carbon dioxide into our atmosphere.
- Solar, wind, hydroelectric and geothermal energy are all renewable forms of energy.
- Fossil fuels are finite and produce carbon dioxide when burned to provide energy.

END-OF-CHAPTER QUESTIONS

The Solar System

1 Draw a simple diagram that shows the positions of the Sun, the planets, the asteroid belt and the Oort cloud in our Solar System

2 Using the table, make scale drawings of the planets Mercury, Venus, Earth and Mars

Planet	Diameter (to nearest 1000 km)
Mercury	5000
Venus	12 000
Earth	13 000
Mars	7000

3 Using the data in the table make a prediction as to the length of a year for a fictional newly discovered planet that lies between Jupiter and Saturn.

Planet	Distance from the Sun (Au*)	Year (in Earth years)	Mean speed (km/s)
Mercury	0.39	0.24	47.89
Venus	0.72	0.62	35.04
Earth	1.00	1.00	29.79
Mars	1.52	1.88	24.14
Jupiter	5.20	11.86	13.06
Saturn	9.54	29.46	9.64
Uranus	19.19	84.01	6.81
Neptune	30.06	164.79	5.43

* 1 AU, 1 astronomical unit is the mean distance between the Earth and the Sun.

Gravity

4 Write down the equation that shows the relationship between weight, mass and gravity.

5 Using the table, calculate the weight of an 870 kg car on the surface of:
   a. Earth
   b. Mars
   c. Jupiter
   d. Neptune.

Planet	Surface gravity (N/kg)
Mercury	4
Venus	9
Earth	10
Mars	4
Jupiter	25
Saturn	10
Uranus	10
Neptune	11

6 Describe the relationship between gravitational field strength and the distance from the surface of a planet.

7 Process the data in the table by changing it into a graph. Make sure you use the most appropriate format, and include a title, axis labels and units.

8 Using the data in the table and your knowledge of the planets in the Solar System, make a prediction as to what the surface gravity might be on the Moon and give a reason for your answer.

Earth

9 Draw a labelled diagram of the internal structure of the Earth showing the locations of the core, the mantle and the crust.

10 Describe what is meant the terms *day* and *year*.

11 Describe and explain what is unusual about the length of a day and a year on Venus.

12 Give an example of each of these rocks:
   a igneous
   b sedimentary
   c metamorphic

13 State what particular conditions are responsible for forming a metamorphic rock.

Extraction of metals

14 Give an example of an ore. State what metal it contains and how it is used today.

15 Describe a method of separating a metal from its ore.

16 Draw a diagram that shows the particle arrangement of a solid, a liquid and a gas.

Living things

17 Using the food web, write down all the food chains you can see.

18 State one essential thing that living organisms need to survive in an environment. Explain why this is needed.

19 Explain these terms:
   a producer
   b primary consumer
   c secondary consumer

20 Using the image, create a key to identify leaves I to VII by their number (you don't need to know the plant names to complete this task).

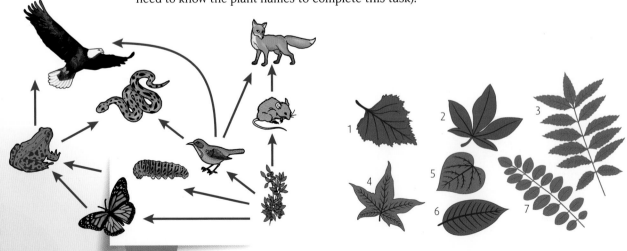

Photosynthesis

21 Write down the word equation for photosynthesis.
22 State the type of energy that is required for photosynthesis to take place.
23 State one factor that affects the rate of photosynthesis in a plant. Give a reason why.

Fertilisers

24 Write down the names of the main minerals that are used in fertilisers.
25 Using information from the 'Lawn Starter' fertiliser label, draw a bar graph showing the ratio of the concentrations of nitrogen, phosphorus and potassium.
26 Give an advantage and a disadvantage of the use of fertilisers.

Climate change

27 Draw a table, with headings 'Renewable' and 'Non-renewable' energy sources. Give at least three different renewable and three different non-renewable energy sources.
28 Which gas in the atmosphere is thought to be mainly responsible for causing climate change?
29 Choose a renewable form of energy. List the advantages and disadvantages of the use of that form of energy in Scotland.
30 Using evidence for your opinion, write down your personal thoughts on climate change – is it a problem or not? Explain why you think this.

TEACHING NOTES

Find teaching notes for these questions at www.brightredpublishing.co.uk

ATHLETE!

Human beings are complex biological machines. Starting from the fusion of two simple cells, a human grows to be capable of extraordinary things.

Athletes are amazing examples of what humans can achieve. Technology allows us to measure the functions of body systems.

An athlete is competing in a triathlon race – she will swim, cycle and run before she reaches the finish line. She has been training for years, constantly pushing her body to give its best performance.

COMPETITIVE SPORT

There is a moment, the split second before a race begins, when the athlete is completely focused and her body is perfectly prepared for what she is about to do. All her muscles are ready, her heart is already pumping fast and adrenaline is pushing through her blood vessels. All her body systems are ready to go.

A pounding heart and racing pulse are familiar sensations to us all. Everyone has felt them when exercising or feeling scared. This is the respiratory and circulatory systems making sure the body has enough oxygen to work properly.

The outcomes and experiences for this chapter are:

I have explored the structure and function of organs and organ systems and can relate this to the basic biological processes required to sustain life. SCN 3–12a

I have explored the role of technology in monitoring health and improving the quality of life. SCN 3–12b

 What's coming up?

* Discovering the respiratory system
* Investigating the circulatory system
* Discussing the digestive system
* Exploring the reproductive system

THE RESPIRATORY SYSTEM

The human body is made up from a variety of **organs** that each contribute to keeping the body alive and healthy. Most organs are part of a body system (a group of organs that work together). One such body system is the **respiratory system**. The lungs are part of the respiratory system. Along with the heart in the circulatory (or cardiovascular) system, the athlete works her lungs hard during her active training.

The primary purpose of the respiratory system is to provide all the cells in the body with the oxygen they need to work properly and to remove carbon dioxide. This happens when the blood flows through the lungs because the carbon dioxide passes through the alveoli and into the lung ready to be breathed out during the next breath.

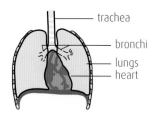

trachea

bronchi

lungs

heart

Gas exchange in an alveolus

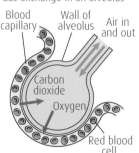

Blood capillary

Wall of alveolus

Air in and out

Carbon dioxide

Oxygen

Red blood cell

We breathe air containing oxygen into our lungs. The air enters the mouth and passes down into the **trachea**, further down into the **bronchi**, then the **bronchioles**, finally reaching the thousands of tiny **alveoli** deep inside the lung tissue.

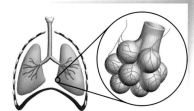

The alveoli are tiny air sacs that are surrounded with small blood vessels. From the alveoli, oxygen is able to enter the blood flowing through the surrounding blood vessels.

 Classroom challenge

Model lungs

Instructions

Using your **processing skills** and whatever materials you have available to you (coloured paper, pens, foam board, balloons, paint), make a model of the lungs. Remember that scientific diagrams and models always include labels.

THE CARDIOVASCULAR SYSTEM

The cardiovascular (or circulatory) system is made up of arteries, veins and the heart, which work together to move all the essential nutrients, gases and chemicals around the body.

The heart is a large hollow muscle. Its job is to **relax** and **contract** in order to pump blood around the body. The heart pumps blood through the lungs in order to pick up oxygen, then through the rest of the body to deliver oxygen to every cell.

DON'T FORGET

Arteries carry blood away from the heart – **A** for **a**rteries, **A** for **a**way. Veins carry blood towards the heart.

Blood is pumped out of the right ventricle into the **pulmonary arteries**, which transport **deoxygenated** blood to the lungs. There, the blood is **oxygenated**. It travels back to the heart via the pulmonary vein to the left atrium.

This blood, now rich in oxygen, passes into the large left ventricle to be pumped out into the aorta (an artery) and round the rest of the body.

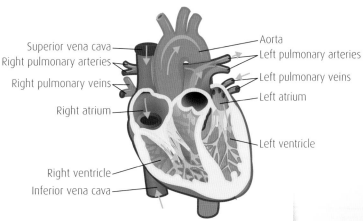

Chambers and blood vessels of the heart, showing directional blood flow

Classroom challenge

Learn more about body systems and use your **researching skills** by completing the Body Systems Homework in the Homework Helpers bundle.

Blood flow through the heart

Instructions

Make a flowchart that shows the movement of the blood through the heart. Make sure you include the names of each part of the heart, in the correct order.

All the answers can be found in the passage on page 99. Make sure you read carefully and use your **selecting skills** wisely!

The blood eventually returns, with the oxygen used up, back to the right atrium and then into the right ventricle to start the process all over again.

MONITORING THE HEART AND LUNGS

In order for our athlete to ensure her training is working to improve her fitness, she needs to monitor her heart and lungs to ensure they are working efficiently.

There are a number of different technologies for monitoring heart and lung function. The stethoscope, a simple piece of equipment, was the first invention for this purpose. You have probably seen one used.

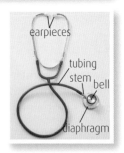

 Did you know?

Fact file: René Laennec

Born	17 February 1781
Died	13 August 1826
Nationality	French
University	University of Paris
Known for	Inventing the stethoscope
Jobs	Doctor working at Hôpital Necker, Paris. Then a lecturer at Collège de France in 1822. Became a professor of medicine in 1823. Finally, he became the head of the medical clinic at Hôpital de la Charité.

René Laennec invented the stethoscope in 1816 in Paris, France. The simple stethoscope is still used 200 years later by nurses and doctors all over the world. The stethoscope is used by placing the 'bell' on the patient's chest while the doctor listens to the naturally amplified heart and lung sounds through the earpieces. It takes years of training to understand the sounds of the heart and lungs, and to be able to diagnose illnesses from these sounds.

More recent inventions include devices that can measure aspects of the respiratory and cardiovascular systems. Some are used in hospitals by medical practitioners to analyse complex signals, others are machines that can be bought and used by members of the public. There are even apps for your smartphone or smartwatch that can monitor your breathing and heart rate (the number of beats your heart completes in one minute) during training.

A **heart rate monitor** is a device that measures the number of times the heart beats every minute. When a person is active their heart rate increases naturally. The body's cells require more oxygen when the body is working hard.

A **pulse oximeter** is a device, normally placed over a finger, which measures the amount of oxygen being carried by the blood. Doctors use this to test whether enough oxygen being transferred in the lungs to the blood.

 ## Classroom challenge

Health monitoring and screening

Aim: To observe the effects of exercise on the human body

Find an extra activity on monitoring the heart rate at www.brightredpublishing.co.uk

Equipment

- Stopwatch
- Pulse oximeter

Heart rate and oxygen level indicate how fit and healthy a person is. These measures can also be used as part of a screening process for heart problems, along with a minor blood test for cholesterol level.

Instructions

1. Check how much oxygen is in your bloodstream at rest and measure your heart rate.
2. Exercise for a set period of time and then take new measurements.

Use a table like Table 10 and your **processing skills** to draw a graph of the results. You should use your own data if you have the equipment to take measurements, but use the example data if you need to.

Once you have drawn your graph use your **predicting skills** determine the oxygen level in blood after 12 minutes.

Table 10 Oxygen levels in blood

Time (mins)	Oxygen saturation of blood during exercise (%)
0	99
2	98
4	97
6	96
8	95
10	95

There is an extra activity on monitoring the heart and lungs in our Homework Helpers: just visit www.brightredpublishing.co.uk for additional questions.

Questions

Use your **researching skills** to answer the following questions.

1 What is cholesterol?
2 How can cholesterol be controlled?
3 What does BMI stand for?
4 What is the normal range of BMI?
5 Why is it important to know a person's BMI?
6 Screening can be used to detect lots of health conditions. What does *screening* mean in this context?
7 Continue using your researching skills to find out the symptoms of:
   a bowel cancer
   b macular degeneration
   c diabetes.
8 How can screening help in the identification of the three conditions you have researched?

TEACHING NOTES

Find teaching notes for this challenge at www. brightredpublishing.co.uk

These pieces of equipment are simple and effective ways to help track fitness and health. Our athlete uses them regularly during her training. She is able to tell how her fitness is improving and even noticed a difference in her heart rate when she became pregnant. Her heart actually beats faster than usual just because she is carrying a baby!

CELLS

It's easy to think of the heart and lungs as *machines* with functions in our bodies. However, these organs are not mechanical appliances like motors. They are made of soft **tissues**, which are made from **cells**.

The outcomes and experiences for this chapter are:

Using a microscope, I have developed my understanding of the structure and variety of cells and of their functions. SCN 3–13a

 ## What's coming up?

- Identifying internal cell structures
- Discovering different types of cells and their jobs
- Investigating the function of a light microscope

WHAT IS A CELL?

Cells are the building blocks of living things. Our bodies are made up from millions of these microscopic units. There are many different kinds of cells in our bodies. Each organ in the body is made up of different types of cells. While these cells have differences, they also have a lot in common.

 ## Did you know?

Invention of the microscope

Cells are so small that you can't see them with your eyes alone. They can only be seen using a microscope. The simple light microscope that we use today was perfected by a scientist called Robert Hooke. He is also the person who invented the term *cell*.

 ## Classroom challenge

Robert Hooke

1. Complete a fact file about Robert Hooke. You should include information about who he was and what he invented and discovered. Include a section on how his invention changed the world.
2. Make your own microscope!

Aim: To construct a small microscope to understand how they work

Equipment

- Two convex lenses
- Piece of paper with text on

Find teaching notes for this challenge at www.brightredpublishing.co.uk

Instructions

1. Take two magnifying glasses.
2. Hold one of them a short distance from a piece of paper with writing on.
3. Take the second magnifying glass and hold that between the first one and your eye.
4. Move the bottom magnifying glass up and down to bring the writing in and out of focus.
5. You have made a simple microscope!

The microscope was an extraordinary scientific invention for the time, but it is actually quite easy to make a simple version for yourself. The light microscopes you will use in class function in a similar way to Robert Hooke's historical invention.

The objective lens (the one you can rotate above the stage) does the job of the first magnifying glass in your homemade microscope. It can also be moved up and down in a way that brings the image you are looking at into focus. The eyepiece does the job of the second magnifying glass from your model and is the lens that focuses the light from the bulb (or mirror) into your eye, so that you can actually see the image.

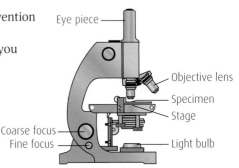

Microscopes need a lot of light to work, which is why there is a light bulb or mirror so that the image you see is bright and clear. The light passes through the **specimen** (thing you are looking at) into the objective lens, up through the eyepiece and into your eye. The focus dials on the side of the microscope turn to bring the image into sharp focus. Everyone sees things in a slightly different way. Changing the focus allows you to see the clearest image for your eyesight!

ANIMAL CELLS

The skin is an organ. Our athlete's skin is made up of simple animal cells with the same main three parts as any other cell. There are some different types of specialised cells that work together to provide all her skin's functions and keep her delicate internal organs safe. The athlete's skin is hard wearing and can recover from damage, like blisters on her feet and grazes on her knees and elbows. By healing, her skin protects her body from infection.

 ## How does that work?

Cell parts

Cells of all types from all animals have the same three parts. For at least part of their lives, they all have:

- a **nucleus**, which contains DNA – the genetic instructions for controlling the cell's activities
- a **cell membrane**, which is the outer boundary of the cell that controls the entry and exit of materials
- **cytoplasm**, which is the site of chemical reactions in the cell.

In addition to these three main parts, there also other cell parts that you will learn about if you study cells in more detail.

This is an image of a few simple skin cells, photographed using a microscope.

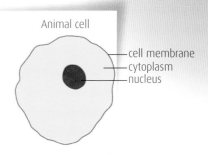

Animal cell

cell membrane
cytoplasm
nucleus

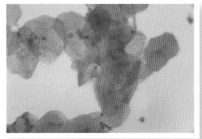

 Classroom challenge

Looking at your own skin cells

Aim: Observation of skin cells using a microscope

Using a microscope, you can look at your own skin cells!
Your mouth is part of your digestive system. The food you eat is chopped up and ground down by the teeth in your mouth. Because of the chewing and scraping, the skin cells in your mouth renew frequently and this means they are very easy to remove.

Equipment

- Microscope
- A clean cotton swab
- A microscope slide and cover slips
- Bromothymol blue stain
- Safety goggles

Instructions

1. Rub the cotton swab up and down on the inside of your cheek.
2. Rub the cell sample on the swab onto the centre of a microscopic slide.
3. Add a single drop of stain called **bromothymol blue**.
4. Place the **cover slip** down carefully. Your teacher will show you how to do this safely.
5. Set your microscope and see what your cells look like!
6. You should record the images in your notes by drawing. Remember that scientific diagrams need labels.

Safety!

Always wear safety goggles.

Bromothymol blue will stain skin and clothing, so avoid spills.

TEACHING NOTES

Head to www. brightredpublishing.co.uk to find the protocol for this experiment.

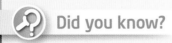 **Did you know?**

Plant and animal cells

Plants are also made of cells. Plant cells have the same simple parts as animal cells doing the same jobs; a nucleus, a cell membrane and cytoplasm.

Simple plant cells have three extra essential parts. These are:

- the **cell wall**, which is made of a stiff substance called cellulose; this gives the cell structure and strength
- **chloroplasts** where photosynthesis happens (see page 141)
- the **vacuole**, which is filled with liquid to keep the cell firm.

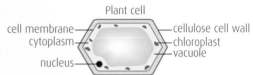

Plant cells face different stresses to animal cells, but in the same way our athlete can put stress on her cells by training hard, plants can deal with the stresses of their environments too.

As the athlete is standing waiting for the race to start, she can feel her skin cells doing their jobs. She can feel the hairs on the back of her neck standing up. The breeze in the air cools the sweaty skin on her forehead. She can feel her heart start to beat faster, so she takes a deep breath to help calm her nerves.

Heart and lung cells have features in common with the simple skin cell, but differences too.

Specific types of cells work together to make tissues, which make up organs. For example, heart cells work together to form heart tissue, which makes up the heart.

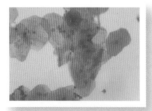

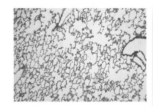

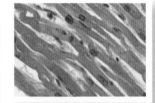

Skin cells   Lung cells   Heart cells

Heart cells have a very different shape compared to normal skin cells. Skin cells are an irregular shape, while heart cells are long and thin, and all run in the same direction. The shape of the cell is related to its function. Muscle tissues need are strong and contract; so muscle cells are long and thin and arranged in a particular pattern.

Lung cells are very thin and flat, and are also able to secrete chemicals that help with the transfer of gases in and out of the blood.

All these cell types start developing before a baby is born!

DIGESTIVE SYSTEM

It is not only the respiratory and circulatory systems that the athlete needs to consider when she is training for an event. Her body is like an engine and just like an engine she needs fuel. Fuel allows all of her different body systems to work normally. Extra healthy fuel helps them work hard and win races.

The athlete needs to think about her digestive system. This is the set of organs that work together to extract the nutrients from the food that she eats to supply her with energy.

The outcomes and experiences for this chapter are:

 By taking part in practical food activities and taking account of current healthy eating advice, I can prepare healthy foods to meet identified needs. HWB 3–30a

 I am developing my understanding of the nutritional needs of people who have different conditions and requirements. HWB 3–32a

 I can explain the links between the energy I use while being physically active, the food I eat, and my health and wellbeing. HWB 3–28a

 ## What's coming up?

- Investigating the energy needs of the human body
- Understanding the different energy needs of different bodies
- Exploring healthy eating

ENERGY REQUIREMENTS

Our athlete has greater energy requirements than a less active person. However, as a female sportsperson her energy needs are less than for a male athlete.

Now she is pregnant, she must increase her energy intake more than usual.

Table 11 Calorific needs of different types of people

	Average calorific daily needs (kcal)
Men (21+)	2700
Women (21+)	2000
Infants	1000–1200
Girls (11+)	1600
Boys (11+)	1800
Pregnant women	2500

Classroom challenge

Different people have different needs

Instructions

Using information from Table 11, answer the following questions about the average number of calories different types of people need. To be successful at answering these you will need to use your **selecting** and **processing** skills.

Questions

1 How many calories does a man need?
2 How many calories does an infant need?
3 How many calories does a 12-year-old girl need?
4 Paula is pregnant. How many calories will she need to eat every day?
5 How many more calories will Paula need to eat than Michele, who is not pregnant?
6 Darren is 55. How many calories will he need to eat?
7 Does Darren need to eat more or less calories than Paula?
8 Chris has a son who is 14 years old. How many calories each will Chris and his son need to eat in a day?
9 How many calories in total will your family need to eat in a day?
10 Exercise uses up calories quickly and our athlete is pregnant like Paula. Paula is not very active. Do you think the athlete will need to eat the same calories as Paula? Why?

DIGESTION

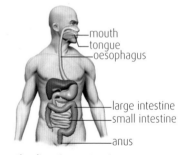

Each different part of the digestive system has different 'looking' cells as they all have different jobs to do. The size of the cells gets smaller as you move from the mouth to the large intestine so that the area that your food comes into contact with gets bigger, meaning there is more time extract as many of the nutrients and water from the food as possible. The cells in your mouth are large and easily removed in order to prevent damage from your teeth when chewing whereas the cells in your large intestine are organised in a completely different way.

Digestion, the process of extracting nutrients from food and taking them into the body, starts in the mouth.

The digestive system is made up of the mouth, oesophagus, stomach, small intestine and large intestine

Cells found in the mouth

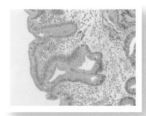
Cells found in the oesophagus

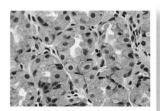
Cells found in the stomach

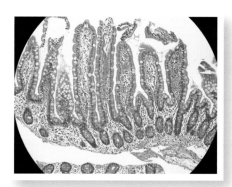

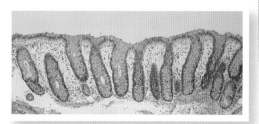

Cells found in the large intestine

Cells found in the small intestine

Food is cut up into smaller pieces by the teeth, so that it can pass safely down the **oesophagus** to the **stomach**.

Once the food enters the stomach, it is broken down further into smaller pieces by a strong acid and chemicals called enzymes. Then it passes into the small intestine.

 ## Did you know?

Stomach acid

Stomach acid has a pH of 1–3. It is such a strong acid that it is as strong as car battery acid and can burn through a piece of wood! It contains potassium chloride, sodium chloride and hydrochloric acid.

The only reason that the acid does not burn through the stomach wall is that it has a thick protective lining. Stomach acid helps to keep us safe from bacterial infection, by stopping microbe growth inside our bodies.

As the food is pushed down the length of the **small intestine**, nutrients are absorbed out of the food, through the intestinal wall and into the bloodstream. Millions of tiny folds called **villi** on the inside wall of the small intestine increase the surface area for efficient absorption.

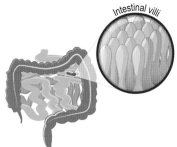

Intestinal villi

Villi in the small intestine

What remains of the food passes into the **large intestine**. Here, water is absorbed through the intestinal wall and the remaining waste is eventually expelled through the **anus**.

Classroom challenge

Make your own poo!

Aim: To build a model for understanding the digestion process

This is a hands-on demonstration activity.

Download the teaching notes for this challenge at www.brightredpublishing.co.uk

Safety!

Do not eat any of the foods.

Method

1 Place all the food in the "mouth" and mash / slice with the "teeth". Add in the "saliva" and the "enzymes". Use the "tongue" to help food into the "stomach".
2 Add "acid" and "enzymes" and then churn the bag.
3 Cut a small hole in the corner of the bag and pass the food into the "small intestine".
4 Add "enzymes", "bile salts" and "sodium bicarbonate" to the mix and pass the food along. Squeeze the nutrients into the appropriate bowl and then use the sponge to illustrate the absorption of the villi.
5 Transfer the mix to the "large intestine". Pour any remaining liquid into the appropriate bowl.
6 Cut a hole in the corner of the bag and transfer remains into the "toilet".

The process of digestion is designed to extract and absorb as many of our food's nutrients as possible. Because our bodies are so good at extracting chemicals from our fuel, we need to be careful about the food we eat.

 Did you know?

A balanced diet

The body needs a variety of different nutrients, as well as enough calories to work properly. Athletes need to consider their energy and nutrient needs in order to maximise their performance.

The NHS publishes advice, based on the findings of scientific studies, about the components of a healthy balanced diet.

One piece of advice is 'five a day'; everyone should eat five portions of fruit and vegetables every single day. Meals should also include a starchy component like potatoes, pasta or rice. This provides the energy your body needs to function properly. The rest of your diet should contain some protein, some dairy and a small amount of fats and oils.

Protein is especially important to young people who are still growing and athletes who want to develop stronger muscles. The stronger your muscles, the better you will be at your sport!

Classroom challenge

Food diary

Instructions

1 Make a food diary over three days of all the food you eat. You should include all meals, snacks and drinks.

2 Read through your food diary and consider whether you have been eating a healthy diet.

3 Using your **processing skills** and the Eatwell Plate designed by the NHS, make a plan for a meal.

4 Write a healthy meal plan for the next three days, including all meals, snacks and drinks. Make sure your diet is balanced but is also varied – this means you shouldn't be eating the same foods every day. Would you actually like to eat all the foods you planned?

5 Look back at your healthy meal plan and your food diary. **Analyse** your entries and pick three items from your food diary that you could change to make your diet healthier.

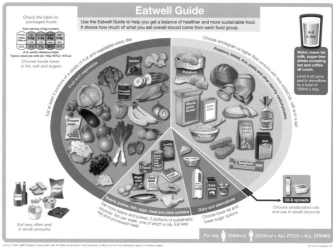

Get cooking!

Planning a meal is the easy part! Try (with permission and supervision) to make your own meal. Plan your meal, source your ingredients, prep your food and cook it!

Use this example recipe to help you plan a healthy meal.

Ingredients

- 50 g/1¾ oz wholegrain long-grain rice
- 1 red and 1 yellow pepper
- low-calorie cooking spray
- 1 small onion, thinly sliced
- 1 courgette, diced
- 75 g/2½ oz cherry tomatoes, halved
- 2 garlic cloves, crushed
- 1 tsp ground cumin
- 1 tsp ground coriander
- 20 g/¾ oz toasted flaked almonds
- ½ orange, zest only, finely grated
- 3 heaped tbsp. roughly chopped fresh flat leaf parsley (or coriander)
- 100 g/3½ oz mild goats' cheese, rind removed and cheese cut into chunks
- salt and freshly ground black pepper.

Method

1　Preheat the oven to 200°C/400F/Gas 6. Cook the rice in a pan of boiling water for 25 minutes, or until just tender, then drain.

2　Meanwhile, cut the peppers in half from top to bottom and discard the seeds. Place, open-side up, on a baking tray (cut a sliver from the base if necessary to help them sit flat). Bake for 15 minutes.

3　Spray a frying pan with cooking spray and cook the onion and courgette over a medium heat, stirring regularly, for 4–5 minutes, or until softened and lightly browned.

4　Add the tomatoes, garlic, cumin and coriander and cook for a minute, stirring constantly. Tip into a large heatproof bowl and stir in the almonds and orange zest.

5　Add the rice and parsley and season with a little salt and lots of pepper. Mix together.

6　Fill the peppers with the rice mixture. Dot with the cheese and return to the oven for 10 minutes, or until the peppers are softened and the filling is piping hot.

> Find at more on the importance of a balanced diet by completing the excercise in the Homework Helpers.

REPRODUCTION

The athlete has been training her body and mind to make sure she can do her best in this race. The fact that she is in the early stages of pregnancy hasn't stopped her from training and competing safely. She has changed her diet to give the nutrients and calories that her body and her developing baby need.

But what does being pregnant actually mean?

The outcomes and experiences for this chapter are:

⟨*I understand the processes of fertilisation and embryonic development and can discuss possible risks to the embryo.*⟩ SCN 3–14a

 What's coming up?

- Discovering the journey of fertilisation
- Investigating the development of an embryo
- Discussing the possible risks of harm to a developing baby

FERTILISATION

Our athlete's baby, or fetus, is growing inside her uterus (sometimes called the womb). The fetus has been developing over the last 19 weeks from a tiny fertilised egg.

Find an extra activity on fertilisation to strengthen your knowledge of this topic at www.brightredpublishing.co.uk

Babies are made by a process called fertilisation. This happens when two cells, one from a male (the sperm) and the other from a female (the egg), join together to create a new cell. The fertilised egg then starts to divide into more and more cells, which will form a baby.

Before we think about fetal development, we are going study where the sperm and the egg come from in the first place.

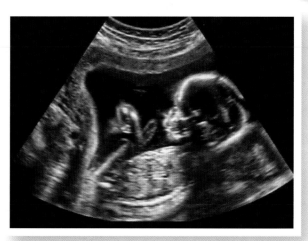
19-week-old embryo

113

FEMALE REPRODUCTIVE SYSTEM

The egg is the female sex cell and contains half of the genetic information required to form a new human being.

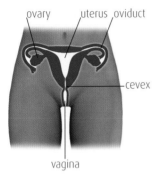

ovary uterus oviduct

cevex

vagina

Female reproductive system

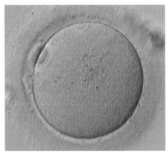

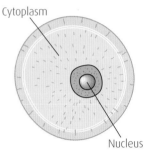

Cytoplasm

Nucleus

An egg cell

Eggs are made and stored in the ovaries. Girls are born with all the eggs they will ever have. These are made when the female fetus is developing and are released gradually during the female's lifetime.

This release happens in a regular pattern, starting once the female reaches **puberty**. Once a month, roughly every 28 days, an egg is released from an **ovary**. It is caught up by the **oviduct** and swept along the tube towards the uterus. In the preceding days, the **uterus** becomes swollen with blood vessels carrying nutrients, so if the egg is fertilised the uterus is ready to nourish the fetus. If there is no pregnancy, these blood vessels are not needed and so are shed from the body through the vagina. This is known as **menstruation** or 'having a period'.

This cycle repeats every month until hormonal changes mean that eggs are no longer released. There are a number of different things that can interrupt this cycle, but the most common one is pregnancy. Pregnancy occurs when the egg cell is fertilised by the sperm cell, usually after **sexual intercourse**.

 Did you know?

In vitro fertilisation (IVF)

There are a number of different ways for egg and sperm cells to meet. The most common method is through intercourse between a male and a female, but this is not the only way to create a baby. There are methods such as In Vitro Fertilization (IVF) and sperm or egg donation.

 **Classroom challenge**

Researching assisted fertilisation

There are many different reasons why people need medical help to conceive a child and various ways of combining sperm and egg cells, meaning that people now start families in all sorts of different ways.

Instructions

Using your **researching skills** investigate one process from the following list:

- IVF
- Egg donation
- Sperm donation
- Surrogacy

Research the basics of how your chosen process works, why it is carried out and the benefits and disadvantages of the procedure.

You should produce a PowerPoint or Prezi or Poster presentation showing your research. Remember to include your sources of information.

MALE REPRODUCTIVE SYSTEM

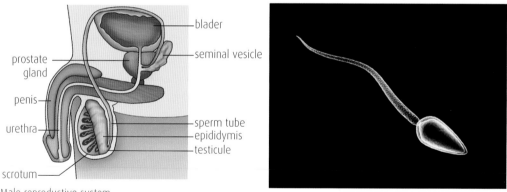

Male reproductive system

Sperm cell

Sperm cells are produced in the male reproductive system. A sperm is much smaller than an egg cell, and sperm are made throughout the male's lifetime. Like the egg, the sperm contains half the genetic information needed to form a new human.

Millions of sperm are produced in the male **testes**, which are held in the **scrotum**. The sperm travel from the testes through a sperm tube where nutrients are added to help the sperm survive. This mixture is called **semen**. To reach the egg cell inside the female's body, semen is ejaculated out of the penis through the **urethra** and into the woman's vagina.

The millions of sperm that are released swim towards the egg. They must travel through the vagina and uterus to meet the egg in the oviduct. If fertilisation occurs here, the process of forming a new human will begin.

There is an extra activity on this topic in our Homework Helpers bundle – just visit the Bright Red website to strengthen your knowledge!

FETAL DEVELOPMENT

From the moment the nuclei of sperm and egg cells join, the process of forming a human begins. It takes approximately 9 months, or 40 weeks, for the ball of cells to develop into a baby.

At the very start of the process, the ball of cells implants into the uterus wall, which has a thick lining of blood vessels that are full of the nutrients the growing **embryo** needs to survive. Over the next eight weeks, the cells of the embryo continue to divide, making more and more cells. These cells specialise and become different tissues; for example, heart tissue and skin. After eight weeks the embryo is known as a **fetus**. The fetus continues to develop until it can survive on the outside of its mother's body.

Embryonic and fetal development takes place inside the mother's uterus, which changes in miraculous ways to support this growth. The placenta forms. In this organ, the mother's and baby's blood comes close enough, without actually mixing, for oxygen and nutrients to pass from mother to fetus. The baby is joined to the placenta by the **umbilical cord**. Without these two structures the baby would not grow.

The amniotic sac forms around the baby and helps to keep it safe during the average of 40 weeks it will spend in the uterus. The sac is filled with amniotic fluid, which cushions the baby against impacts from the outside world.

FERTILISATION PROCESS

Fertilisation and embryo diagram

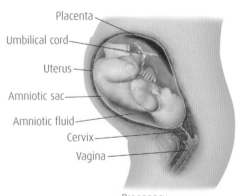

Placenta
Umbilical cord
Uterus
Amniotic sac
Amniotic fluid
Cervix
Vagina

Pregnancy

 ## Classroom challenge

Information leaflet

Instructions

Use your **selecting skills** and the information in this section make an informational leaflet that shows the process of fetal development. You should make your leaflet eye catching and full of information. Here is a suggested plan:

- Page 1 (front page) – title page and introduction
- Page 2 – what happens during the embryo stage
- Page 3 – about the fetus
- Page 4 (back page) – questions that the reader could go away and find out for themselves

You should include accounts of the main changes during the embryonic and fetal stages. You might find these words and phrases help to get started:

- embryo
- ball of cells
- tissues
- fetus
- development
- survival.

Since the fetus gains nutrients from the mother, via the umbilical cord, it is important for the mother to eat healthily. Chemicals from every food the mother puts into her body are passed to the baby.

Other aspects of the mother's lifestyle can affect the developing fetus too. For example, smoking cigarettes lowers the amount of oxygen in the mother's bloodstream, which means the baby will receive less oxygen from the placenta. This can lead to small babies who are born too soon.

Drinking alcohol during pregnancy can harm the developing baby's nervous system, especially its brain, causing a condition known as **fetal alcohol syndrome**.

Download the Homework Helpers for an additional activity on fetal development.

Our athlete will need to ensure she is eating enough calories to fuel her training and healthy foods to ensure her body has all the nutrients it needs to support her growing baby.

GENETICS AND DNA

When we studied the fertilisation process, we learned that half of the genetic information to build a person comes from the mother's egg, and the other half comes from the father's sperm.

This **genetic information** is stored in a very long and complex chemical called DNA (**deoxyribonucleic acid**). DNA has two strands that weave around one another in a shape known as a double helix. It includes a code to tell your cells how to work and what to do. Your special code is what makes you unique.

The outcomes and experiences for **this chapter are**:

I have extracted DNA and understand its function. I can express an informed view of the risks and benefits of DNA profiling. SCN 3–14b

What's coming up?

- Discovering the function of DNA
- Exploring the idea of a DNA database
- Extracting DNA experimentally

Our athlete's unique DNA code has made her naturally athletic. She has long arms and legs, strong muscle tissues and an efficient digestive system, meaning that she is naturally more suited to competing in races. She trains to enhance her natural abilities.

Does her DNA code mean that she has an unfair advantage? This is a topic of debate in a number of different sports. When top athletes' DNA codes are examined, they seem to have codes that make their bodies ideally suited to their sport.

STRUCTURE OF DNA

DON'T FORGET

'Always take great care' when remembering which bases are paired up. **Always** (adenine) **take** (thymine; A and T pair up) **great** (guanine) **care** (cytosine; G and C pair up).

Codes are not always easy to read. The code in DNA comes from four chemicals known as bases. They are **cytosine**, **guanine**, **adenine** and **thymine**. They pair up so adenine and thymine are always linked together and, in the same way, cytosine links with guanine.

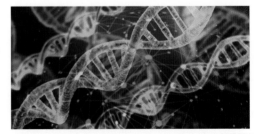

DNA structure diagram

The sequence of the bases in your DNA makes up the code that instructs your cells how to grow and function. DNA is the reason your eyes are a certain colour and your feet are a particular size. It also controls many other aspects of your appearance, including whether you can roll your tongue. You are the result of your DNA code!

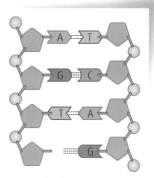

Base-pairs diagram

 Classroom challenge

Experiment to extract DNA

Aim: To extract DNA from a soft fruit

Equipment

- Beaker
- Test tube
- Wooden skewer
- Masher/blender
- Dish soap
- Pineapple juice
- Ethanol (ice cold)
- Soft fruit (banana)

—DNA

Instructions

1 Add the banana to a beaker and mash until smooth.
2 Add 5 ml of liquid dish soap to the mashed banana and mix thoroughly. Try to avoid creating bubbles.
3 Add three drops of pineapple juice to the banana/soap solution.
4 Transfer the mixture to a test tube.
5 Very slowly, pour cold ethanol down the side of the test tube. This should be done at an angle to create a layer of ethanol on top of the banana/soap mixture.
6 Leave to stand for 5 minutes.
7 Observe a white substance that is suspended between the two liquid layers.
8 Very carefully, using the wooden skewer, hook out some of the white substance and transfer it to a microscope slide.
9 Observe the extracted DNA under the microscope.

Safety!

Always wear eye protection.

Avoid skin contact with ethanol. Wash off spills with water

Find teaching notes for this challenge at www. brightredpublishing.co.uk

Classroom challenge

Unravel the code

The diagram shows a simplified version of the DNA code – only one strand of the double helix is shown and short sequences of bases represent genes for different physical characteristics.

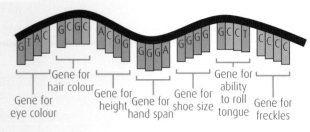

Gene for eye colour
Gene for hair colour
Gene for height
Gene for hand span
Gene for shoe size
Gene for ability to roll tongue
Gene for freckles

Table 12 Code for eye colour

Colour	Brown	Blue	Grey	Green
Matching gene code	GTAC	CTAG	TAGC	ACGT

Table 13 Code for hair colour

Colour	Light blonde	Dark blonde	Light brown	Dark brown	Black
Matching gene code	ACTG	TAAT	CCGT	GCGC	CGGT

Table 14 Code for height

Height (cm)	<130	131–140	141–150	151–160	161–170	171–180
Matching gene code	AAGG	CTCC	TGGT	ACAC	ACGG	GAGA

Table 15 Code for hand span

Span (cm)	<12	13	14	15	16	17	18	> 19
Matching gene code	GCCG	CCCT	TCTG	CGGC	CTCG	GGGA	GAAA	CGTG

Table 16 Code for shoe size

Size	<3	3	4	5	6	7	8	9	10>
Matching gene code	TTAT	TATA	GGGG	CTAG	GACA	ACTG	GTCA	AAGG	CCGG

Table 17 Code for ability to tongue roll

Ability	Yes	No
Matching gene code	ACCG	GCCT

Table 18 Code for presence and location of freckles

Position	None	Cheeks	On nose	On Nose and cheeks
Gene code	CCCC	CAAG	GTCG	ACTG

Instructions

1 Using your **selecting skills**, read the code for each gene on the simplified DNA strand and find the matching code in the appropriate table.

2 You should be able to work out what the person with this DNA code will look like.

3 Draw the person into your notes, using the correct coloured pencils and including the information you cannot draw in a fact file next to your drawing.

DNA PROFILING

As every single human has a different DNA code, will some people be better at some things than others?

 Did you know?

DNA profiling activity

Everyone has a different DNA code. The unique information in DNA can be collected and stored as a DNA profile. DNA profiles can help the police solve crimes, people to find lost family members and even to find out about possible health issues before they develop.

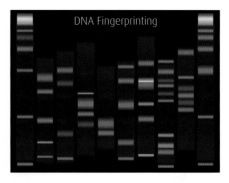

DNA Fingerprinting

 Classroom challenge

Instructions

Using your **researching skills**, use the internet to research the different uses of DNA profiles and DNA databases.

At the end of your research use your **analysing skills** and consider your opinion on DNA profiling and databases. Do you think DNA databases are good or bad? Should everyone have to give a sample of their DNA to a database? Would you be happy if your DNA was stored? Write a paragraph giving your opinions on these issues and your reasons for feeling the way you do.

 Did you know?

Fact file: Michael Phelps

Michael Phelps is one of the best swimmers in the world. At time of writing, he has won 28 Olympic medals and has competed in all the elite competitions. Does Michael Phelps have some physical advantages which help him to swim so fast?

He is 6 feet 4 inches (1.93 m) tall, an ideal height for a competitive swimmer. More interestingly, his arm span (the length from middle finger to middle finger) is 6 feet 7 inches (2.01 m), so his arm span is longer than his body. This means he has exceptional pulling power through the water.

He has size 14 feet. This size is slightly bigger than average, but since his joints are extra flexible he can move his feet more in the water. Having large feet that are easy to move is like wearing flippers when you swim!

Michael Phelps was born with these physical attributes that are in his DNA code. He trains hard to develop elite fitness and a flawless technique, but his genetic code has definitely helped make him a very successful swimmer.

 Classroom challenge

Use your literacy skills

Instructions

You should use the skills you have been learning in school to write a convincing essay stating your personal opinion on this topic: *'Athletes are only good at their sports because of their genetics.'*

This type of writing is called persuasive writing and in science it must be based on **scientific fact**.

Using the information in this chapter and other information you have found from reliable internet sources, decide whether you agree with the topic statement. You are entitled to your own opinion but you must support your case with facts.

MICROBES

Our athlete must consider all aspects of her health and fitness. She has been doing cardiovascular workouts to help train her heart and lungs for racing. She is eating the correct types of foods and gaining the appropriate amount of energy for training and to meet her growing baby's needs. She also understands her advantages based on her genetics. She should be aware of, and in control of, her exposure to microbes.

The outcomes and experiences for this chapter are:

I have contributed to investigations into the different types of micro-organisms and can explain how their growth can be controlled. SCN 3–13b

I have explored how the body defends itself against disease and can describe how vaccines can provide protection. SCN 3–13c

 ## What's coming up?

- Investigating micro-organisms
- Discussing the differences between bacteria, fungi and viruses
- Exploring the immune response in humans
- Discovering vaccinations

BACTERIA, FUNGI AND VIRUSES

Our athlete's body is full of microbes! Although certain microbes pose a risk to her health, she actually needs some of them to help her body work at its best.

Microbes are microscopic forms of life, meaning that we need a microscope to see them. There are three groupings of microscopic life:

- bacteria
- viruses
- fungi

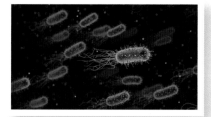
Bacteria

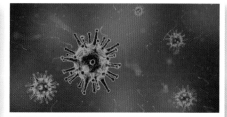
Virus

Microbes are found everywhere! There are more microbes than all other forms of life put together.

Bacteria

Bacteria are organisms consisting of just one cell. They have no nucleus, a cell membrane and are filled with cytoplasm. They divide and multiply very quickly. On average, there is one cell division every 20 minutes – they increase in number very quickly when the conditions are right.

 Classroom challenge

Microbe experiment

Aim: To demonstrate that microbes are found in the classroom

Equipment

- Nutrient agar plate
- Pen (for labelling)
- Cotton swab
- Sticky tape
- Disposal bin

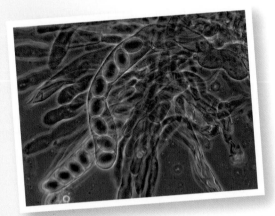

Fungus

Instructions

1. Collect a nutrient agar plate and write your name and the date on one edge of the bottom.
2. Draw a cross along the bottom of your plate to make four separate sections.
3. Take four cotton swabs, to sample four different areas of the classroom. Before proceeding, discuss with your teacher which areas are acceptable for sampling and why. Next, use a swab to sample an area by wiping it on the area.
4. Lightly run the swab onto the surface of the nutrient agar and label that section of the plate with where the sample was taken.
5. Dispose of cotton swab immediately.
6. Using the remaining three cotton swabs, repeat the process for the three more areas of the classroom.
7. Place lid on agar plate.
8. Using two small pieces of sticky tape, secure the lid in place. **Do not seal completely.**
9. Return your labelled plates to your teacher for incubation.
10. Your teacher will place the plates into an incubator at a suitable temperature to grow bacteria. You will see the results in a day or two!

Using the information in the photo caption and your **processing skills**, answer the following questions.

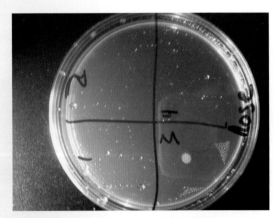

Bacteria reproduce at regular time intervals. Remember that every 20 minutes the number of bacteria cells doubles!

Questions

1. If there are 100 bacteria in a Petri dish, how many will there be 20 minutes later?
2. If the conditions are right, how many of the same bacterial cells will there be 60 minutes later?
3. If there 1000 bacterial cells present on a surface at 1 pm, how many would there have been at 12:40 pm?
4. If the conditions remained right, how many of these same cells would there be at 3 pm?

TEACHING NOTES

Find teaching notes for this challenge at www.brightredpublishing.co.uk

There are lots of types of bacteria and they exist in many different shapes and sizes. Some are harmful and can cause bacterial infection, while others are harmless or even helpful.

Did you know?

You are covered in bacteria!

While some bacteria can be potentially harmful to you if they get inside your body, your skin is actually covered in hundreds of millions of them. There are also healthy, essential species that live in your digestive system and help break down foods.

Probiotic yoghurts (containing helpful bacteria) are sold in supermarkets for us to eat. Scientists do not fully understood how they work, but think they help to maintain a healthy balance of gut bacteria that help digest food and reduce numbers of harmful bacteria.

Fungi

Fungi are also single-celled organisms but tend to be bigger than bacterial cells. They are found everywhere and there are over 99 000 known types of fungus. They can grow by themselves (like mushrooms) or on other things (like moulds). They are very useful to the environment and to humans. Yeast is a very common type of fungus and we use that in the everyday process of making bread, beer and wine. In the environment, fungi help to break down dead plants and animals.

Viruses

Viruses are the smallest type of microbe. Viruses are simply strands of genetic material encased in a protein coat. They can only reproduce when they are inside a host cell. Because they can't reproduce on their own, some scientists believe they are not really living organisms.

PREVENTING INFECTION

When some types of microbes enter our bodies, this is an infection. Only some infections lead to disease and/or illness.

Our athlete has travelled all over the world for training and competing in triathlons. If the wrong type of microbe enters her body she could get sick, which could put her training back and possibly endanger her baby.

Our bodies can act as the perfect **habitat** for microbes to reproduce and multiply in number. They produce **toxins** inside our bodies, making us feel ill and causing **disease**. We use medicines like **antibiotics**, **antivirals** and **antifungals** to help our bodies fight off these infections.

 Classroom challenge

Antibiotic ring experiment (demonstration)

Aim: To investigate the effect of type of antibiotic on bacterial growth

Instructions

You will not usually be allowed to carry out this experiment, but your teacher may show you some results (there is a link to some results in the Teaching Notes). Use your **processing skills** to explain what has happened.

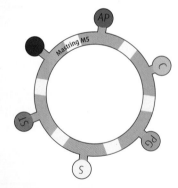

The Petri dish was filled with nutrient agar, and then bacteria was spread on top of the agar. A paper ring with arms and discs was used. Each disc was soaked in a different antibiotic and the ring was placed on top of the bacteria. The plate was incubated for several days.

A large clear area around a disc indicates that the antibiotic has prevented bacterial growth. The smaller the area around the antibiotic disc, the less effective the antibiotic.

Find teaching notes for this challenge at www.brightredpublishing.co.uk

Write a conclusion explaining these experimental results. Remember that the aim of the experiment was to investigate the effect of type of antibiotic on bacterial growth.

Download the Homework Helpers from www.brightredpublishing.co.uk for an extra activity on fungal infection and cell structure.

Vaccinations

Vaccines are very effective at helping our bodies fight off harmful diseases. A vaccine, made from an inactivated or simplified microbe, is injected into the body. This gives the

immune system a chance to learn how to fight the disease without actually making the person ill. Most children have a series of vaccinations during their first 12 months of life and then again before they start school. Chances are you have been vaccinated already!

Vaccinations are successful at protecting against harmful diseases because they work with the body's natural immune responses. The immune system deals with microbe invaders – a number of organs, tissues and cells all work together.

White blood cells are one part of this immune system:

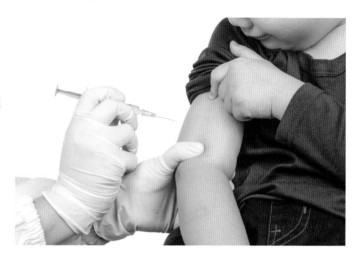

- one type of white blood cell destroys invading germs
- the other type 'remembers' germs from past encounters and can respond quickly if the body is invaded again.

When you are vaccinated with an inactivated or simplified version of a microbe, you don't become ill but your body makes the type of white blood cell that remembers how to fight that infection. If you are exposed to the real microbe in the future, your body already knows how to fight it and you don't get the symptoms of the infection.

 ## Classroom challenge

Comic strip presents: *Vaccines*

Find out more about vaccination and test your **researching skills** by completing the Homework Helper activity at www.brightredpublishing.co.uk

Instructions

Using the internet and your **researching skills,** find out how vaccinations work with the body's immune system to promote health. You should take notes from this research.

Make a comic strip about how the vaccinations work. Make sure your sources of information are reliable!

Hygiene

The best way to reduce the chance of harmful infection is to stop microbes entering the body in the first place. There are a number of ways in which microbes can enter our bodies, but we have natural defences against this. We can also help to decrease the chance of infection with good hygiene habits.

Microbes are everywhere: on our bodies, on surfaces all around us and on the food we eat.

It is important wash hands properly with antibacterial soap after using the toilet, to ensure that microbes from inside our bodies don't contaminate the areas around us and get into our food.

When preparing food, it is also important to wash our hands so that microbes don't get into our food.

There is an extra activity on this topic in our Homework Helpers bundle.

When we sustain an injury, like a cut, microbes can enter our skin through the open wound. It is important to clean the wound with an antibacterial liquid and dress the wound with a plaster or bandage to stop bacteria entering the wound before the skin has healed.

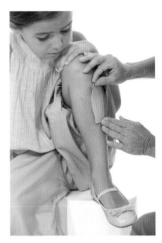

Treating injuries

USEFUL MICROBES

Microbes can be very useful to us. We have already learned there types of bacteria that live inside us which are beneficial to our digestive process and which reduce numbers of harmful bacteria.

We also use microbes in industry.

Baking and brewing

Yeast, a fungus, is used in baking and brewing. Yeast produces the gases to make bread rise and makes the alcohol in beer and wine.

Rising bread

Insulin

We produce the chemical insulin in our bodies to regulate the sugar content of our blood. Some people with a condition called diabetes are not able to produce their own insulin and have to inject it to stay healthy. Previously, this insulin came from pigs. Nowadays bacteria and yeast are used to make synthetic insulin for treatment of diabetes.

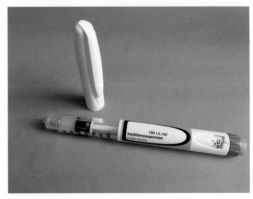

Insulin for treatment of diabetes

pH

She's ready. Her feet are just over the edge of the pool. This is the moment she has been preparing for. Her heart, lungs and muscles are trained to peak fitness. She will push herself harder than she has ever pushed before and maybe, just maybe, she will win this race and the medal she has been dreaming about for so long.

She hears the instruction to take her mark. The starting pistol fires with a loud pop and she dives head first into the clear blue water of the swimming pool.

The outcomes and experiences for this chapter are:

Having taken part in practical activities to compare the properties of acids and bases, I have demonstrated ways of measuring and adjusting pH and can describe the significance of pH in everyday life. SCN 3–18a

What's coming up?

- Discovering the pH Scale
- Investigating the effects of adding acid and alkali together

SCIENCE OF A SWIMMING POOL

What has a swimming pool to do with science? There are actually loads of things about swimming that are science related. Let's take a look at microbes, for example.

Swimming pools are busy places, bustling with people and their microbes. Being warm and damp, pools could provide perfect conditions for microbes to grow. Fortunately, pool water is treated with chlorine granules. Chlorine is toxic to most microbes, so it keeps the swimming pool clean and free of bacteria.

pH

Like all living things, microbes require particular environment conditions to thrive. One of these conditions is for the **pH** to be at the correct level.

pH is a measure of how acidic or alkaline a substance is on a scale of 0 to 14. Acidic substances have a pH level of 0 to 6.9, whereas alkaline substances have a pH between 7.1 and 14. A pH of 7 is **neutral**.

This is measured using a chemical called Universal Indicator which is a mixture of different chemicals that change colour gradually over a range of pH's. This can be used as a liquid or on paper; known as pH paper. In liquid form the indicator can be added directly to what you want to check the pH of and pH paper can be dipped into a liquid sample.

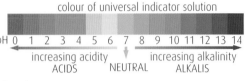

colour of universal indicator solution

pH 0 1 2 3 4 5 6 7 8 9 10 11 12 13 14

increasing acidity → ↓ ← increasing alkalinity

ACIDS   NEUTRAL   ALKALIS

pH scale

Most microbes do best in an environment where the pH is between 6.5 and 7, that is where the pH is near to neutral.

 Did you know?

Complete the exercise on acids and alkali and build on your knowledge by downloading the Homework Helpers from the Bright Red website.

Extremophiles

Some microbes, called extremophiles, can survive in very acidic conditions with a pH of 1. Hydrothermal vents, which are like volcanoes on the seabed, have very acidic conditions. There are hundreds of species that live in the water around these vents – scientists had not expected to find life here.

When our athlete is in the pool, she will be swimming in water with a controlled pH of between 6.2 and 6.8. This pH is harmful to microbes but not to humans.

Human skin is tolerant of a range of pHs. The pH of a substance can be tested using a chemical called **Universal indicator**. This is a green liquid that changes colour depending on the pH of the test substance. Stomach acid would turn Universal indicator red and drain cleaner would turn it purple. The colour that Universal indicator turns can be matched to a reference chart, so we can tell the pH of any chemical.

 Classroom challenge

pH poster

Instructions

Take a piece of A4 paper and, turning it to landscape, draw the pH scale from 0 to 14 in the middle of the page. Fill the entire length of the page but only about one-third of the depth. Colour the scale correctly.

Now test a variety of different household chemicals using Universal indicator. Record the colour change and pH number for each chemical in a table of results. Use sensible column headings and a ruler to draw the table lines.

Now using your **selecting skills** add the names of the household cleaners to your pH scale poster, making sure you match the pH result you found to the correct colour and number on the scale.

Most microbes need to live in a place that remains in the neutral section of the pH scale.

As the athlete is standing poolside, she takes a deep breath. She smells the familiar odour of the swimming pool caused by chlorine. The chlorine is added to the pool in order to change the pH of the water from neutral to slightly alkaline. The ideal pH of pool water is 7.4, which is a small, almost unnoticeable, difference for humans, but causes huge problems for microbes and prevents their growth.

 ## Classroom challenge

Optimum pH

Table 19 shows different microbes and their optimum pH for survival. Optimum pH is the pH level that bacteria can survive at, if the pH was to increase or decrease by 0.1 then the bacteria would not survive. All of these microbes would cause us to become unwell if we accidently ingested them while swimming.

Table 19 Microbes and their optimum pH

Species	Optimum pH
Salmonella	7.9
Clostridium botulinum	7.2
Escherichia coli	7.6
Campylobacter	8.1
Shigella	7.5

Strengthen your knowledge of this topic by downloading the Homework Helpers at www.brightredpublishing.co.uk and completing the practice exercise on the pH scale.

Questions

Look at the starting pH of the water in questions 1–5 below. Use your **processing skills** to calculate by how much the pH would need to change in order to kill *all* the different microbes in Table 19.

Then answer questions 6–9.

1 pH = 7.1
2 pH = 7.9
3 pH = 7.2
4 pH = 6.9
5 pH = 6.7
6 Which of the species would survive in a pH of 8.1?
7 Which species has the lowest optimum pH?
8 Make a graph of the table of results. Decide on the best type of graph to draw. Make sure you label your axes and use a suitable scale.
9 Choose one of the species and use your **researching skills** to find out about the symptoms of the disease this microbe causes.

There is a balance between acids and alkalis. You can change the pH of a substance by adding a substance from the other side of the pH scale to it. This is how the swimming pool pH is maintained to keep it safe for humans but harmful to microbes, it's called Neutralisation. It is called this because when you add an acid and alkali together you can make a neutral substance. It's like a balance: you can make exactly the pH you would like if you add exactly the right volumes of acid and alkali together.

 ## Classroom challenge

Neutralisation experiment

Aim: to find out what happens when an acid and an alkali are added together

Equipment:

- Test tubes
- dropper
- 0.1M Hydrochloric Acid
- 0.1M Sodium Hydroxide
- Universal Indicator

There is an extra activity in our Homework Helpers to help you practise and revise this topic.

Instructions

1 Using a dropper add five drops of alkali to a test tube
2 Add two drops of Universal Indicator
3 Record the colour and pH
4 Add five drops of acid to the test tube
5 Record what happens to the colour of the Universal indicator.

Safety!

Students should wear safety goggles at all times while acids and alkalis are being handled

If any acids or alkali are spilt onto skin, wash thoroughly with water.

Now try to make a test-tube rainbow!

Safety!

Wear eye protection throughout.

Test-tube rainbow

 ## TEACHING NOTES

Find teaching notes for this challenge at www. brightredpublishing.co.uk

FORCES

As the athlete is swimming, she controls her arms and legs which are working hard to pull her through the water. Her body knows what to do. Everything is going to plan, she is in second place.

She knows not to go too fast, in case she tires herself out before the next section of the race. As she reaches the end of her swim, she pulls herself out of the water onto the poolside. She pauses for a fraction of a second, then jumps onto her bike for the second leg of her triathlon race.

Her bike ride is all about forces; from the force of her muscles pushing down on the pedals, to the forces between the tyres and the road, to the air resistance that makes her ride harder or easier depending on the way the wind blows.

The outcomes and experiences for this chapter are:

By contributing to investigations of energy loss due to friction, I can suggest ways of improving the efficiency of moving systems. SCN 3–07a

 What's coming up?

- Discovering what forces are
- Exploring the effects of friction
- Exploring balanced and unbalanced forces

WHAT IS A FORCE?

A force is a push or a pull. A force can cause an object to change its speed, its direction of travel or even its shape.

A If you push the ball, it starts to roll

B If you push against the motion of the ball, you can stop it

C If you push at an angle to the ball's motion, you can change the direction of the motion

D If you apply balanced forces, you merely squeeze the ball

Forces can change an object's speed, direction of travel or shape

133

Classroom challenge

Playing with forces

Instructions

1 Take a small ball of modelling clay, playdough or blue tack.
2 Roll it into as smooth a ball as possible.
3 Use the diagram for ideas about how to experiment with the forces you can put on the ball.

Forces are measured in units called newton (N), named after Sir Isaac Newton who worked on the concept of forces in the seventeenth century. Remember when we looked at weight as a force on different planets (page 46)? We were using newton there too.

 Did you know?

Fact file: Sir Isaac Newton

Born	4 January 1643, Woolsthorpe, England
Died	31 March 1727 (aged 84), London, England
Nationality	English
Notable works	*Opticks* *The Mathematical Principles of Natural Philosophy* *The Method of Fluxions and Infinite Series*
Subjects of study	Light Colour Planets Calculus Newton's laws of motion

Sir Isaac Newton, English physicist and mathematician

We can use a newton balance or other more modern force meters to measure the size of forces in Newtons.

Newton balance and modern force meter

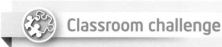 **Classroom challenge**

Measuring forces

Aim: To measure the force required to pull an object along a surface

Instructions

1. Choose 10 objects of varying size and mass.
2. Using the force meters that are available in your classroom, find out what force is required to move each object.
3. Draw a results table with the headings 'Object' and 'Force required (N)'. Record all of your results into this table.
4. Draw a bar graph showing your results.

 **TEACHING NOTES**

Find teaching notes for this challenge at www.brightredpublishing.co.uk

BALANCED AND UNBALANCED FORCES

When our athlete is in the triathlon, she is both applying and working against forces.

When she is cycling, she pushes the pedals to turn the wheels of her bike, producing a forward force that propels the bicycle. Her efforts are countered by friction forces: air pushes against her body and bike as she moves forwards and there is also friction between the surface of the road and the bike tyres, and friction in the moving parts of the bike. These friction forces slow her forwards motion down.

As in the case of the cyclist and bike, there are often many forces acting on an object at one time. When these forces are equal in size but opposite in direction, we call them **balanced forces**.

When forces are not equal and/or not in opposition, we call them unbalanced forces

Forces acting on a bike

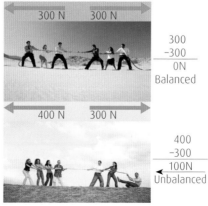

300 N   300 N

300
−300
‾‾‾‾
0N
Balanced

400 N   300 N

400
−300
‾‾‾‾
100N
Unbalanced

Balanced and unbalanced forces

Balanced and unbalanced forces have different effects on the motion of the body they are acting on:

- If forces on an object are balanced, the object will either remain still or continue to move with a constant speed.
- If forces are unbalanced, the object will accelerate in the direction of the greater force.

For our athlete to accelerate forwards when swimming, running or cycling, she must produce a larger forwards force than the opposing backwards frictional force.

 Classroom challenge

Calculations involving forces

Questions

Use your **processing skills** to work out the direction of travel (left, right or no movement) and size of force for each of the objects below.

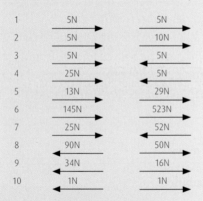

Investigating forces

Aim: To investigate the effect of mass on the force required to move an object

Design your own experiment to investigate this aim.

Instructions

1. Write a method explaining how to carry out an investigation to show that the more mass an object has the more force is required to move it.
2. Include clear step-by-step instructions, a diagram and a list of the equipment needed to carry out the experiment. Make sure that your instructions are clear and easy to understand. Imagine you are writing them for a primary school pupil. You need to tell them exactly what you want them to do, because they have never done an experiment like this before!

FRICTION

Friction is a force that opposes motion. Two different types of friction are air friction and surface friction.

- Air friction is the force of the air particles pushing on a moving object as it travels through the air.
- Surface friction happens when moving surfaces run together, such as when an object moves across a surface or as moving parts of an object rub.

Friction produces heat.

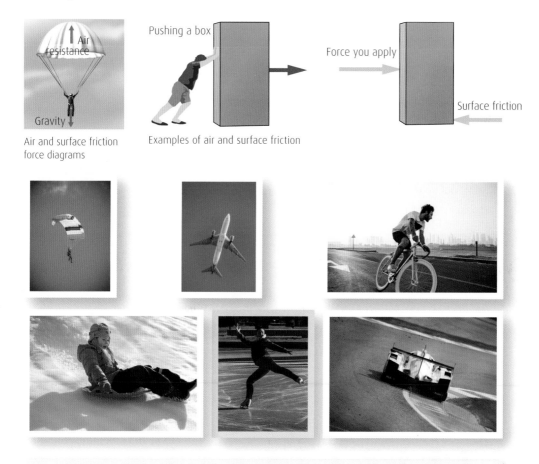

Air and surface friction force diagrams

Examples of air and surface friction

Air friction is our athlete's enemy. It slows her down and she has to work hard to keep her speed the same. She must keep a steady pace so that she doesn't get too tired before the end of her race. She needs to reduce the amount of air friction she has to work against.

REDUCING FRICTION

Sports scientists put a lot of effort into reducing the friction forces acting on the athletes.
Reducing friction helps increase the speed of the athlete.

There are different ways of reducing friction, depending on the type of friction under consideration.

Reducing air friction

Air friction is caused by air particles hitting the object as it moves. To reduce the force of air friction acting on an object, the object's shape needs to be streamlined. This means the shape of the object is changed so that air is pushed around rather than against the object.

Consider the streamlined shape of a sports car compared to the angular shape of a bus. The bus has a large flat front surface that the air strikes, whereas the sports car has curved surfaces that guide the air around the chassis.

Bus and sports car diagrams showing frictional forces

Athletes achieve streamlining of their body shape mainly through the clothes that they wear when competing. Athletes tend to use very tight-fitting outfits. Loose and baggy clothes would act like a parachute and catch the air, slowing the person down.

An athlete's streamlined clothes smooth out their body shape

Reducing surface friction

Our athlete needs a certain amount of surface friction to allow her to grip and push forwards off the track. With no surface friction she would just slip without control.

Runners wear spikes on their shoes to ensure a good grip with the track. Bicycle tyres also have treads that grip the road.

However, bikes also have moving parts where friction occurs, reducing their efficiency. Friction occurs where the wheels move around the axle and where the chain moves over the sprockets.

To reduce unwanted frictional forces, we use lubricating liquids, like oil. Oil makes surfaces smoother so that they are able to slip over each other more easily.

Oil on gears

Visit www.brightredpublishing.co.uk and download the Homework Helpers bundle for an extra activity on reducing friction.

Classroom challenge

Design your own athletics outfit

Instructions

1 Choose any sport.
2 Using your **analysing skills** design an outfit that a competitor in that sport could wear. You need to think about what parts of the outfit would catch the wind and cause air resistance. In some sports this might be useful; in others it would be a problem to be minimised!
3 Draw your design. All scientific diagrams should include labels to tell what each part is!

THE FINISH LINE

Her body has worked so hard swimming and cycling, and now she is starting to feel tired. Her muscles are aching but she pushes herself on to the next stage.

She is taking big deep breaths as she parks her bike in the stand. She glances down at her laces to check she is ready to run and takes off. She pushes from one foot to the other, breathing deeply and starting to count.

Her shoes are designed to grip the track, without causing unnecessary friction. She uses her knowledge of forces to make sure she is working efficiently and not creating too much air resistance.

She took probiotics with her balanced breakfast this morning, to ensure her body is able to use all the nutrients and energy from her diet. She has enough healthy fuel in her body to get her past the finish line in good time.

Her body's immune system is protecting her against infections, her genetics have coded for her long limbs and strong muscles and her heart is pumping the oxygen she breathes in through her lungs to her tiring muscles.

Her front foot passes the line. She's done it. The race is over. She trained to swim, cycle and run to the best of her ability. She's a winner!

Problem-solving skills developed

I can:

- use my creativity to effectively communicate a scientific idea
- select relevant information to complete a complicated scientific diagram
- research a given topic and select, edit and reword my findings
- select information from a table of information
- process information in a table to form a valid conclusion
- analyse information from an infographic to form a valid conclusion
- research a given topic to communicate advantages and disadvantages
- select information from a diagram and use it to read a table and select a correct answer
- research a given topic to form my own opinion, using scientific fact to back that opinion up
- process information to perform a calculation
- process information to form a valid conclusion
- draw a graph from a set of experimental results
- plan an experiment to answer a given aim
- analyse a set of conditions to aid in a creative design process.

 What you now know

Respiratory and cardiovascular systems
- The lungs are part of the respiratory system and the heart is part of the cardiovascular system.
- The lungs allow oxygen from the air to enter the blood. They also allow carbon dioxide to pass out of the blood.
- The heart is a muscle that moves oxygenated blood from the lungs to the rest of the body, and pushes deoxygenated blood back to the lungs.
- Our heart rate is the number of times our heart beats in one minute.
- Exercise increases our pulse rate so that our cells get more oxygen to allow our body to work harder.

Digestive system
- The digestive system comprises the mouth, oesophagus, stomach, small intestine and large intestine.
- The function of our digestive system is to digest the food we take in.
- Food provides nutrients and energy to help our bodies function.
- The stomach contains acid to help to break down food, so that it is easier to digest. It also kills some of the microbes we ingest and provides the correct pH for digestive enzymes to work.
- The small intestine is where chemicals from the food are absorbed into the blood.
- The large intestine is where water is removed from the food.

Reproductive system
- The male sex cell is the sperm cell. Sperm are produced in large quantities in the testes.

- A sperm cell has a head and a tail. The tail allows the cell to move towards the egg cell.
- The female sex cell is the egg cell. Egg cells are produced and stored in the ovaries.
- An egg cell is released from the ovary and moves down the oviduct where a sperm cell might fertilise it.
- A fertilised egg cell can implant into the uterus wall, where the cell will begin to divide and develop into an embryo and then a fetus.

Cells

- Cells are the building blocks of living things.
- A simple animal cell consists of a cell membrane, inside which is cytoplasm and the nucleus.
- The cell membrane controls the movement of substances in and out of the cell.
- The nucleus controls the functions of the cell. DNA is contained in the nucleus.
- A plant cell also contains a cell membrane, cytoplasm and a nucleus. Additionally, it contains a vacuole and chloroplasts, and is surrounded by a cell wall.
- Chloroplasts contain chlorophyll, a chemical that can absorb the light energy needed for the process of photosynthesis.

Micro-organisms

- Micro-organisms are tiny life forms that can generally only be seen using a microscope.
- Bacteria are single-celled organisms. They divide and multiply rapidly given the correct conditions.
- Fungi is a group of micro-organisms that include moulds and yeasts.
- Viruses are much smaller organisms that invade host cells to survive.
- Micro-organisms are often associated with infections and illness. However, some are useful to humans, such as in the making of insulin.

pH

- The pH scale is a way of measuring the acidity or alkalinity of a substance.
- Substances with a pH of 0–6 are acidic, with pH 1 being the most acidic.
- pH 7 substances are neutral. Water is an example of a neutral substance.
- Substances with a pH of 8–14 are alkaline, with pH 14 being the most alkaline.
- pH paper or Universal indicator, along with a colour chart, can be used to determine the pH of a substance.

Forces

- A force is a push or a pull that can change the speed, direction or shape of an object.
- Forces are measured in newton, N. Forces are measured using a force meter or newton balance.
- Balanced forces are forces acting on an object that are equal in size and opposite in direction.
- Unbalanced forces are forces that are not equal in size or opposite in direction, resulting in movement of the object in the direction of the unbalanced force.
- Friction forces are forces that oppose the movement of an object. Air and surface friction both slow an object down.
- Frictional forces can be reduced by streamlining or lubrication.

END-OF-CHAPTER QUESTIONS

The cardiovascular system

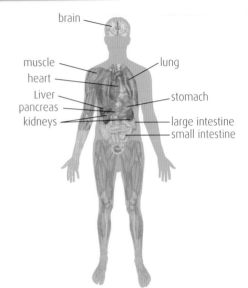

brain
muscle
heart
Liver
pancreas
kidneys
lung
stomach
large intestine
small intestine

1   Using the diagram, complete the following table of organ systems by writing each organ in the right column.

Respiratory system	Digestive system

2   What gas is added to your blood when you breathe in?

3   Describe function of the heart and lungs making sure you use the following key words in your description:

- blood
- oxygen
- carbon dioxide
- cells

4   Name the numbered parts of lung diagram.

5   Name the chambers A, B, C, and D in the heart diagram by picking from the following list:

- left ventricle
- right ventricle
- left atrium
- right atrium

6   Arteries and veins both transport blood around the body. Describe the difference between the blood carried by arteries and the blood carried by veins.

7   Asthma is a condition suffered by many people across the world. Using your **researching skills** find out how asthma affects the lungs.

8   Using your **researching skills**, find out who invented the stethoscope and when? Include some details on what it was used for and how it changed the way doctors could diagnose some illnesses.

9   Using your **researching skills**, draw a diagram of a stethoscope and label the following parts:

- earpiece
- tube
- open bell
- closed bell

10 Using your **researching skills**, find out why there are two bells on a stethoscope. What does the doctor use each bell for?

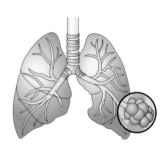

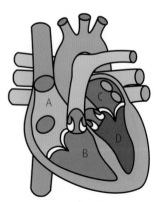

11 A person's heart rate or pulse is the number of times the heart beats in a minute. Write a sentence to describe the relationship between heart rate and activity level.

12 By experiment or using your **researching skills**, find out what does a pulse oximeter does. Why is it important for doctors to be able to measure this characteristic?

Cells

13 Draw a picture of a simple animal cell and label the following parts: nucleus, cell membrane, cytoplasm.

14 Copy and complete the following table to describe the functions of the three major parts of a simple animal cell.

Cell organ	Function
Nucleus	
Cell membrane	
Cytoplasm	

15 There are many more cell parts (organelles). Using your **researching skills**, find out the name of another organelle found in animal cells and describe its function.

16 DNA is found inside the nucleus. Describe its role in the cell.

17 Draw a diagram of a plant cell and label the following structures: nucleus, cell wall, cell membrane, cytoplasm, vacuole, chloroplasts.

18 Copy and complete the following table to describe the functions of the six major parts of a plant cell.

Cell organ	Function
Nucleus	
Cell wall	
Cell membrane	
Cytoplasm	
Vacuole	
Chloroplasts	

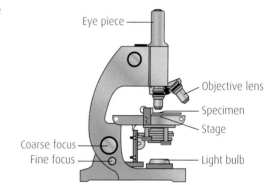

Eye piece — Objective lens — Specimen — Stage — Coarse focus — Fine focus — Light bulb

19 Using your **researching skills**, find out the name of the substance that chloroplasts contain which absorbs light energy.

20 Microscopes are often used to magnify cells or microbes to allow us to study their structures. Using the diagram, describe how you would use a microscope to view onion cells.

21 Describe what happens to the image when you switch between different objective lenses on the microscope.

22 Using your **researching skills** find out what Isaac Newton was famous for discovering. Include in your description some details on when and how his discovery was made.

The digestive system

23 Using the diagram to the right, name the five parts A, B, C and D of the digestive system.

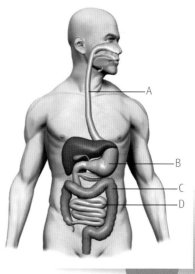

24 The small intestine and the large intestine have different functions in the digestive system. Describe their functions.

25 Describe the journey of a piece of food as it travels through the digestive system. Make sure you explain what happens to the food at each organ.

26 What is the pH of stomach acid? Explain why there is acid in the stomach and how this aids digestion.

27 Make a list of the food and drinks you have had so far today. Using your **researching skills** find out approximately how many calories of energy you have taken in. Show your results in a table like the one below.

Food (and approximate quantity)	Calories (Kcal)
Total =	

28 Complete the table to show the recommended number of calories for each type of person.

	Recommended calories (kCal)
Adult female	
Adult male	
11–14 female	
11–14 male	

29 Why does a pregnant woman need to eat more calories than a woman who is not pregnant?

The reproductive system

30 Label the parts A, B and C of the diagram of the male reproductive system.

31 Name the part of the male reproductive system where sperm are formed.

32 Name the parts A, B, C and D in the female reproductive system in the diagram.

33 Describe the journey of an egg cell from the moment it is released. Include in your description an account of what happens if the egg is fertilised or and what happens if it is not.

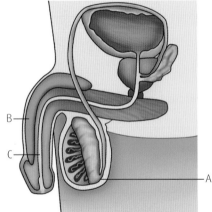

Microbes

34 Draw a simple diagram of a sperm cell, labelling the head and the tail. Why does the sperm cell have a tail?

35 Using your **researching skills**, describe how insulin is made by microbes for people who need insulin treatment for diabetes.

36 Describe the impact the ability to make insulin using this process has had on those who suffer from diabetes.

37 Penicillin is an important antibiotic medicine that has saved millions of lives. Describe what an antibiotic does.

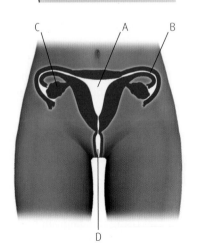

38 Using your **researching skills** find out who discovered the effects of penicillin as an antibiotic. Try to find out how this discovery was made.

39 What are the names of the four bases that make up the DNA code?

pH

40 The pH scale is from 0–14. Give the pH values associated with an acid, an alkali and a neutral substance.

41 Using your **researching skills**, or through a simple experiment, find out the pH of the following drinks.

Drink	pH
Tea	
Orange juice	
Lemon juice	
Cola	

42 Describe how to measure the pH of a substance.

Forces

43 Describe the three effects that a force can have on an object. Give an example of each effect in an everyday situation.

44 Name five different activities from your daily life that are affected by forces. What impact do they have?

45 Forces can be balanced or unbalanced. Describe what we mean by *balanced* and *unbalanced* forces.

46 What is a frictional force? Give some examples of friction in a moving car.

47 Which of the diagrams show balanced and which show unbalanced forces? For each, describe the resulting motion using the following phrases:

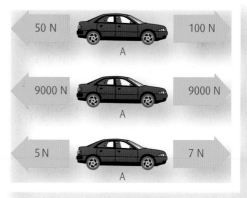

- moving with a constant speed
- accelerating to the left
- accelerating to the right

48 Name all the forces that act on a bicycle. Draw a diagram that shows the names of the forces and their direction.

49 Describe ways of reducing a cyclist's air friction and the surface friction present on a bicycle.

50 Michael Phelps is an Olympian swimmer (see page 121). Describe how he could reduce the friction forces acting against him while he swims.

FALLOUT!

It's only a short time after the catastrophic event – a nuclear war – that changed my life. They say that bombs were detonated all around the world, instantly wiping out whole cities.

Nuclear fallout, the radioactive dust that blasts into the atmosphere and falls far from the site of the explosion, made people so sick. There were many deaths. Even now, the air is dry and hot. Every breath I take is filled with dust that coats my mouth and itches the back of my throat.

I don't understand why this has happened. Did the war fix the problems we had before? What were they thinking when they pushed the nuclear button?

Am I the only survivor? Am I safe? What do I do now?

SEPARATING MIXTURES

I need a drink. I don't have many supplies and I know I will need a water supply to survive. There is an old well not too far from here. It has a covered top, so I think it's safe from the fallout.

I tie my bucket to a rope and pull the cover off the well. I lower my bucket down until I feel it hit the water. I keep lowering the rope until I feel the bucket is heavy with water. I heave it back up.

My heart sinks when I see the contents of my bucket. The water is dirty, full of mud. Then I have a moment of inspiration. It's okay, I know I can fix this. Water can be cleaned. I am going to filter the water.

The outcomes and experiences for this chapter are:

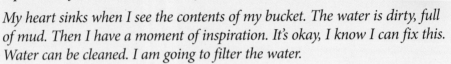

❝I can differentiate between pure substances and mixtures in common use and can select appropriate physical methods for separating mixtures into their components.❞ SCN 3–16a

 What's coming up?

- Identifying elements present in compounds from simple molecular formulae
- Giving examples of pure substances and mixtures from everyday life
- Selecting appropriate physical methods (for example, distillation, filtration and chromatography) to separate mixtures into their components and justifying the choice

FILTRATION

Filtering is a way to remove large particles from a liquid. It is a physical separation technique that can be used to remove impurities from water.

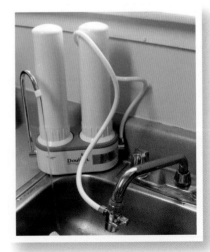

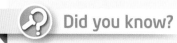

Did you know?

Clean drinking water

Did you know 750 million people around the world do not have access to clean water to drink? These people have to filter their drinking water to ensure they don't get ill. There are different ways to filter water.

The LifeStraw® is a simple invention. It filters out harmful viruses and bacteria from dirty water before it reaches the mouth.

The water from the well is full of stones and mud. I can't drink it like this. I'll take it back to the hut where I have the things I will need to make it safe to drink. I can build my own water filtration system. I will need some sand, some charcoal and a piece of cloth.

Using the internet, research some water purification systems such as the LifeStraw, the Solarball and ceramic water filters

Classroom challenge

Water filtration experiment

Aim: To make your own water filtration system

Equipment

Cotton wool
Gravel
Clean sand
Activated charcoal
Filter paper
Bottle bottom

- A plastic bottle, cut in half and with cap still attached
- Gravel
- Activated charcoal
- Filter paper
- Clean sand
- Cotton wool
- Dirty water

Instructions

1 Take the top half of the bottle and place it upside down into the bottom part of the bottle, as shown in the picture.
2 Place cotton wool in the neck of the upturned bottle (closest to the cap) and place the filter paper on top.
3 Add the activated charcoal on top of the filter paper.
4 Then add a layer of gravel.
5 The sand is added next. The sand layer should be about the same depth as the initial layers combined.
6 Finish off with another layer of gravel.
7 Take the filtration system out of the bottom part of the bottle and remove the cap.
8 Replace the filter set-up in the bottom part of the bottle. Add dirty water to the top.
9 Record your observations of the water that has passed through the filtration system.

Find teaching notes for this challenge at www.brightredpublishing.co.uk

The filter works by catching particles of different sizes in the different filter sections. The dirt gets trapped in the sand, charcoal and paper layers, so that clean water falls through the tiny gaps in the system and into the container underneath. Charcoal is especially good at attracting impurities, which stick to its surface. Filtration can be a simple as using a sieve and separating rocks from sand or filter paper and a funnel, or as complicated as the water filter systems you have looked at.

EVAPORATION, CONDENSATION AND DISTILLATION

The water is not safe to drink yet. I know about microbes and I'm not going to let them make me ill. I can't afford to be sick – I need all my strength.

I need to boil the filtered water to kill the microbes.

*The best way to make sure there is nothing but water in my drinking supply is to evaporate it to steam. Then I need to catch the steam in a clean container and cool it, also known as **condensing**, so it returns to liquid water. This final product will be fresh clean water that is safe to drink.*

I know that water boils at 100 °C. To reach that temperature, I will need a fire.

 Did you know?

Making whisky

Distillation is a way to separate different liquids with varying boiling points. Whisky, which is made by distillation, is one of Scotland's leading exports.

The first stage in making whisky is mixing water, yeast and sugar (or a grain containing sugar) in a container for a number of days. The yeast ferments the sugar to make an alcohol called ethanol.

Once the ethanol has been made, the fermented mixture is moved to a distillation chamber. Here it is heated up so the ethanol can be separated from the other substances in the mix.

The ethanol and water in the mix can be separated as they have different boiling points (the boiling point is the temperature at which a liquid becomes a gas). Water boils at 100 °C and ethanol boils at 76 °C. The ethanol gas escapes first, having the lower boiling point, and moves up the distillation chamber until it cools down and turns back into a liquid which can be collected. The ethanol is stored in wooden barrels for a number of years before it is sold as whisky.

Evaporation is not only a simple way to make sure your water is clean. It can be used to get back a solute, or dissolved solid. That is how you would get salt out of salt water. When the water is heated until it boils and evaporates the salt is left behind and you would see a solid in the bottom of your container. This is the most effective way (of the techniques you will look at) to remove salt from water.

 ## Classroom challenge

Separation techniques poster

You already know a bit about filtration and distillation, which involved evaporation and condensation. Now you are going to use your **researching skills** to find out about chromatography and other uses for evaporation. You can use all this information to make a poster.

Instructions

1. Divide an A4 page into four sections, each with a heading: Filtration, Chromatography, Evaporation, Distillation.
2. Using what you know about filtration, fill in the first quarter page. You should explain how filtration works, perhaps add a diagram and give an example of when you would use this technique.
3. Complete the other page sections by explaining the separation techniques and say how they are used. **Research** using the internet and other available resources.

SOLVENTS

Sometimes I daydream about before the war when I had a choice of things to drink. I torture myself thinking about iced water, diluting juice, tea, milk and fruit juice. I can almost taste my favourite tropical juice! I always made it with too much water – I should have made it stronger.

The outcomes and experiences for this chapter are:

I can take part in practical investigations into solubility using different solvents and can apply what I have learned to solve every day practical problems. SCN 3–16b

 What's coming up?

- Investigating and describing the solubility of substances in different solvents, for example, water and acetone/propanone
- Explaining the link between the relative quantity of solute or solvent and changes in the concentration of a solution

SOLUTIONS

Concentration

Diluting juice is a liquid mixture made up of a solvent (water) and solutes (all the chemicals in fruit juice). You can change the concentration of diluting juice by adding more solvent or water; that is by diluting it.

When a solute is dissolved in a solvent, the solute particles move into the spaces between the particles of the solvent.

Making a solution is making a mixture of solvent and solute, it is not the same as carrying out a chemical reaction. In a chemical reaction new substances are formed.

Substances that won't dissolve into a solvent are said to be **insoluble**.

You can make a solution stronger (more concentrated) by adding more solute. Think about diluting juice. The juice is sometimes called the 'concentrate', because it is a concentrated solution of fruit juice. The concentrate is diluted by adding solvent (water). The solution becomes less concentrated and the taste is weaker.

Classroom challenge

Dilute to taste

Everyone likes their juice solutions at different concentrations. What concentration do you prefer?

Instructions

1   Using **clean** droppers and measuring cylinders, make different concentrations of diluting juice. Make the juice solutions carefully using the volumes set out in Table 20.

Table 20 Diluting juice concentrations

Volume of juice (ml)	Volume of water (ml)	Total volume (ml)
0	10	10
2	8	10
4	6	10
6	4	10
8	2	10
10	0	10

 TEACHING NOTES

Find teaching notes for this challenge at www. brightredpublishing.co.uk

2   Add the drinks of different strengths to labelled plastic cups.
3   Take a sip of the most dilute sample first. Allow it to sit on your tongue and think about the flavour.
4   Once you have swallowed it, take a sip of pure water.
5   Repeat this process with all the dilutions of juice, finishing with the most concentrated.
6   Which concentration of juice do you prefer?

 DON'T FORGET

Safety! Ensure droppers and measuring cylinders are new or completely clean.

OTHER SOLVENTS

Water is not the only solvent that can be used to make solutions. Any liquid that can dissolve a solute is a solvent.

Water does not remove nail varnish, which is why it can be worn for days at a time. Nail varnish does need to be removed eventually so a solvent is required. The solvent dissolves the nail polish, which is the solute, making a solution of nail polish and remover which can be wiped off the nail.

 Classroom challenge

Which solvent works?

Any liquid can be used as a solvent, but not all solvents work with every solute! Do you know the name of the solvent that is used in nail varnish remover? Carry out an experiment to find out which solvent is used in nail varnish remover. You should enter your results in a table with appropriate headings. Your results will be observations, which should be clear and detailed descriptions of what you see.

Solvent experiment

Aim: To find out which solvent works as a nail varnish remover

Equipment

- Glass rods with approximately 2 cm at one end painted with nail varnish
- Four small beakers
- 25 ml each of: water, 0.1 M hydrochloric acid, 0.1 M sodium hydroxide, acetone
- Paper towels

Instructions

1 Label the four beakers, each with the name of one of the solvents.
2 Place 25 ml of a solvent in each beaker.
3 Place a glass rod with nail varnish on the end into the solvent, ensuring the nail varnish is submerged in the liquid.
4 Leave for 5 minutes.
5 Remove the glass rods and place on a paper towel.
6 Record your observations.

Safety!

Solvents are harmful if ingested and can irritate eyes and skin. Wear eye protection throughout the activity.

Practice on this topic further by completing the solvents exercise in our Homework Helpers at www.brightredpublishing.co.uk

TEACHING NOTES

Find teaching notes for this challenge at www.brightredpublishing.co.uk

THE PERIODIC TABLE

If I am to survive, I need to be able to make use of the materials around me. I can remember the Periodic Table, an infographic about the elements that make up the Universe. This scientific information might help decide how to use materials.

The outcomes and experiences for this chapter are:

《*I can consider the properties and uses of a variety of elements relative to their positions when discussing the Periodic Table.* 》 SCN 3–15a

 What's coming up?

- Investigating and describing properties of metals and non-metals, for example, appearance, conductivity of electricity, position in the Periodic Table, and their uses linked to their properties
- Knowing that elements are organised in the Periodic Table by atomic number, each with its own unique symbol, and that elements with similar chemical properties are placed together in vertical groups
- Identifying and naming the groups Alkali metals, Halogens and Noble gases, and describing their reactivity.
- Investigating and describing at least two examples of compounds with properties that are different from their constituent elements, for example, sodium chloride from sodium and chlorine and the electrolysis of copper chloride

ELEMENTS, MIXTURES AND COMPOUNDS

As we already know diluting juice is a **mixture** of fruit juice chemicals and water. A **compound** consists of two or more atoms chemically joined together. Water is a compound of hydrogen and oxygen.

The differences between mixtures and compounds are clear if you understand the basic building blocks of the Universe – **elements**. An element is a substance that is made entirely from one type of atom. There are more than 100 elements that we know of.

Table 21 outlines the differences between elements, mixtures and compounds.

Table 21 Definitions and examples

	Definition	Example
Element	The primary part of matter, an element consists of one type of atom and cannot be broken down into a simpler substance	Hydrogen, Helium, Lithium, Beryllium, Boron, Carbon
Mixture	A combination of different, chemically distinct, substances which can be separated	Blood, cement, mud, smog
Compound	A substance made up of two or more elements that are chemically joined together	Carbon dioxide, sodium chloride, carbon monoxide, sulfur dioxide, water

WHAT IS THE PERIODIC TABLE?

The Periodic Table is an ordered, organised list of all of the elements found on our planet, grouped according to their properties. For example, the elements are split into non-metals and metals.

When you understand how to read it, the Periodic Table can give you lots of useful information. It gives information about the makeup of each element's atoms, as well as an indication of the elements' properties.

 ## Did you know?

Dmitri Mendeleev

Dmitri Mendeleev wrote a version of the Periodic Table in 1869, as shown in the diagram. His version was shorter than the one we use now, because not all of the elements had been discovered when he wrote it.

However, he managed to correctly order the elements he did know about and he even left spaces for the ones he thought would be discovered in the future!

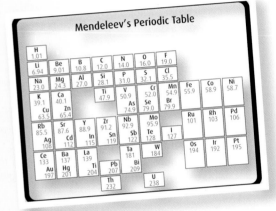

Mendeleev's Periodic Table from 1869

GROUPS OF THE PERIODIC TABLE

Mendeleev was the first person to put the known elements into columns, or **groups**, of substances with similar properties.

Mendeleev considered properties such as how each element reacts with other materials. Elements in the same group react in a similar way with particular substances. The further an element is located towards the bottom of the table or towards the bottom of a group, the more reactive it is.

The elements are arranged in order of atomic mass (number protons + neutrons), reading from left to right like a book. The table also shows the atomic number (number of protons) of each element.

Each and every element is represented by its own unique symbol.

Dmitri Mendeleev

The Periodic Table that we use now is thought to be complete, containing every known element.

Find a new activity on the group of the periodic table in the Homework Helpers at www.brightredpublishing.co.uk

Group

Period	1	2	TRANSITION METALS										3	4	5	6	7	0
1	1 H																	2 He
2	3 Li	4 Be											5 B	6 C	7 N	8 O	9 F	10 Ne
3	11 Na	12 Mg											13 Al	14 Si	15 P	16 S	17 Cl	18 Ar
4	19 K	20 Ca	21 Sc · 22 Ti · 23 V · 24 Cr · 25 Mn · 26 Fe · 27 Co · 28 Ni · 29 Cu · 30 Zn										31 Ga	32 Ge	33 As	34 Se	35 Br	36 Kr
5	37 Rb	38 Sr	39 Y · 40 Zr · 41 Nb · 42 Mo · 43 Tc · 44 Ru · 45 Rh · 46 Pd · 47 Ag · 48 Cd										49 In	50 Sn	51 Sb	52 Te	53 I	54 Xe
6	55 Cs	56 Ba	72 Hf · 73 Ta · 74 W · 75 Re · 76 Os · 77 Ir · 78 Pt · 79 Au · 80 Hg										81 Tl	82 Pb	83 Bi	84 Po	85 At	86 Rn
7	87 Fr	88 Ra	104 Rf · 105 Db · 106 Sg · 107 Bh · 108 Hs · 109 Mt · 110 Ds · 111 Rg · 112 Cn										113 Uut	114 Fl	115 Uup	116 Lv	117 Uus	118 Uuo

metals ← → non-metals

Lanthanides	57 La	58 Ce	59 Pr	60 Nd	61 Pm	62 Sm	63 Eu	64 Gd	65 Tb	66 Dy	67 Ho	68 Er	69 Tm	70 Yb	71 Lu
Actinides	89 Ac	90 Th	91 Pa	92 U	93 Np	94 Pu	95 Am	96 Cm	97 Bk	98 Cf	99 Es	100 Fm	101 Md	102 No	103 Lr

WHAT IS RADIOACTIVITY?

Radioactivity is a property of some of the elements at the bottom of the Periodic Table.

Radioactive elements release energy when their atomic nuclei undergo change.

Radioactive samples are usually labelled with a special symbol to show that they are dangerous.

Radioactive symbol

The atom

Elements are made up of only one type of atom. Atoms are the tiny basic building blocks of all materials. Some larger atoms can be seen with a very strong specialist microscope.

Everything in the Universe is made from atoms which have the same three parts:

- electrons
- protons
- neutrons

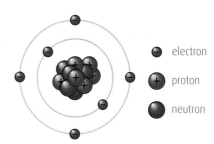

- electron
- proton
- neutron

carbon atom

Parts of the atom

The central part of an atom is called the **nucleus**. This contains two types of very small **subatomic particles** – protons and neutrons. These are so small that you can't actually see them with any kind of microscope.

Protons and neutrons give the atom its mass. There are even smaller parts of an atom: the electrons. These are so small they are considered not to have any mass. Electrons can move from one place to another. This property allows us to produce electricity.

The atoms at the end of the Periodic Table are very heavy with lots of subatomic particles. These atoms can't exist for very long because they are not very stable. An unstable atom must become stable and it does this by losing subatomic particles. The atom ejects some protons and neutrons, or some electrons (amongst other things) to make itself stable. When an element does this, it is said to be radioactive.

Nuclear explosions

Nuclear explosions happen when atoms either break apart or join together. Atoms are so small it is hard to imagine they can cause such devastation. But atomic explosions give out massive amounts of energy.

Elements such as uranium and plutonium have relatively large unstable nuclei, making them radioactive. When these atoms emit radiation, they expel particles from their large nuclei, as well as some energy. We say the atom has **decayed**.

Nuclear mushroom cloud

When radioactive decay occurs in the presence of other unstable atoms, the release of the particles from one atom can cause neighbouring atoms to decay at the same time. The decay spreads through the atoms of the unstable material causing a **chain reaction**.

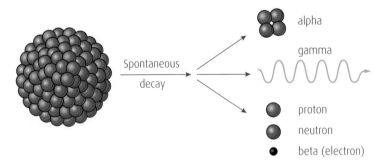

When millions of atoms all decay in a very short space of time due to a chain reaction, a huge amount of energy is released, resulting in a nuclear explosion.

OTHER PROPERTIES OF ELEMENTS

Radioactivity isn't the only property of elements. The way the Periodic Table is organised is based on the way elements react with different substances. Those that react in a similar way are grouped together.

The elements in Group 1, called the **alkali metals**, all react in the same way with water. They are also very reactive with Oxygen. They must be stored under oil, so that the Oxygen in the air doesn't react with them. All the Group 1 elements get very hot when they come into contact with water, causing Hydrogen gas to be formed. As this heats up, it catches fire.

All the alkali metals react like this, but the reactions go at different rates. As you move down the group from Lithium to Sodium to Potassium and so on, the reaction gets bigger; the elements are more reactive further down the group.

| 1st Neutron generation | 2nd Neutron generation | 3rd Neutron generation |

Sodium

Potassium

Using the Periodic Table

The alkali metals are not the only group on the Periodic Table. Each group has its own different set of properties and reactions. When reading the Periodic Table it can be read in either Periods or groups. Periods go along the table (like you are reading a book) and groups go down the Table in columns. When we talk about the Alkali Metals we are reading the first column of the Table, Group 1. The other groups are similar to Group 1 in the sense that they all react in a similar way to each other. Some of the groups have names to help identify them:

Group 1 – Alkali Metals
Group 2 – Alkaline Earth Metals
Group 7 – Halogens
Group 8 – Noble Gases
Middle Block – Transition Metals

Each of these groups exhibit different properties, for example The Noble Gases in Group 8 are interesting because they won't react with any other element; the exist by themselves and will not react. This property means the Group 8 elements are 'inert' or unreactive.

The Group 7 elements, known as the Halogens are interesting because they show the opposite pattern of reactivity in their Group to the Group 1 elements. Where the last element in the Alkali metals is the most reactive the halogens are the opposite and the first element in that Group, Fluorine, is actually the most reactive. The name Halogen refers to the ability to make a salt, when the Halogens react with a metal they form a chemical called a salt.

 ## Did you know?

The most common example of this is table salt.

Sodium (which is a metal) reacts with Chlorine (a Halogen) to form Sodium Chloride. This is the same salt you put on your food. We eat the product of this reaction; isn't it strange to think that a soft, silvery metal reacts with a colourless gas to make the salt you eat on your chips?

Chemical equation   Sodium + Chlorine ⇨ Sodium Chloride
Reactants   **Product**

Another reaction involving Chlorine that is interesting to look at because the reactants are so different to the products the electrolysis of copper chloride.

Copper Chloride ⇨ Copper + Chlorine
Product   **Reactants**

This bright blue solution can be turned back into copper metal and chlorine gas, just by adding electrical energy. The copper metal forms a thick reddish brown solid and the chlorine gas bubbles through the solution.

When you read the Periodic Table and look more closely at all the different element on there you will start to notice more information about them on each tile.

The symbol (Na) is the shorthand way to write the name. This is used to write chemical formula and equations but it is just a shorted way of saying the elements whole name – Sodium. The smaller of the two numbers is known as the Atomic Number, which tell the scientist

11
Na
22.99

reading it that there are that many protons in the nucleus of that atom. Sodium for example has 11 protons in its nucleus. The bigger of the two numbers is called the Mass number and this tell us how much mass the atom has. Remember back to Impact! where you learnt about mass?

 ## Classroom challenge

Head to the Bright Red website and download the Homework Helpers for an additional activity on the Periodic Table and metals/non-metals.

Using the Periodic Table

Questions

As you can see the Periodic Table can give you lots of information about the different elements, from what is inside them to how they will react with the world around them, even if they are radioactive. Use your **processing**, and **selecting skills** to answer the following questions.

1   What is the name of the group of elements in the last column of the table?
2   Which group number is also known as the alkali earth metals?
3   Which elements do not react with other elements?
4   Use the Periodic Table to find out the atomic number of the following elements:
   a   Magnesium (Mg)
   b   Carbon (C)
   c   Aluminium (Al)
   d   Zinc (Zn)
   e   Iron (Fe)
5   Use the Periodic Table to find out the mass number of the following elements:
   a   Lithium (Li)
   b   Neon (Ne)
   c   Gold (Au)
   d   Thorium (Th)
   e   Boron (B)
6   Use the Periodic Table to determine which element is the most reactive of the Halogens.
7   Use the Periodic Table to determine which element is the least reactive of the Alkali Metals.
8   Use the Periodic Table to determine which element forms a group with Gold (Au) and Silver (Ag).
9   Use the Periodic Table to determine which of these elements would be the most reactive: Boron (B) Silicon (Si) or Arsenic (As)?
10   Use the Periodic Table to find the name of five radioactive elements.

Instructions

1   Using the Periodic Tables that are available in your classroom and on the internet and your **selecting skills**, produce a poster for each of the different groups on the Periodic Table; Alkali Metals, Alkali Earth Metals, Transition Metals, Halogens and Noble Gases.
2   Make sure your poster includes the group name and number.
3   Include the names and atomic numbers of the elements within each group and give an example of a use for each of the elements you name.

HEAT TRANSFER

The filtered and distilled water feels crisp on my tongue. It's better than the drinks in my daydream!

Now I need to think about my other needs. The nights are getting colder, so I must make sure I stay warm. This hut could make a great shelter as long as I can keep it cosy. I can't just turn up the heating like I could at home.

I'll build a fire and collect plenty of wood to keep it going. It's really too hard to start a fire so I'll try not to let it go out at all. I'll add enough wood to keep the fire burning right through the night.

I've found suitable materials for insulation and I am fairly certain that I can keep the warmth from the fire within the building.

The outcomes and experiences for this chapter are:

❝*I can use my knowledge of the different ways in which heat is transferred between hot and cold objects and the thermal conductivity of materials to improve energy efficiency in buildings or other systems.*❞ SCN 3–04a

What's coming up?

- Applying knowledge from practical investigations to explain how heat is transferred by conduction, convection and radiation
- Establishing a link between heat loss in a building and the temperature difference between the inside and outside of the building
- Applying understanding of thermal energy efficiency, conductors and insulators to explain how materials can be used in building design to reduce heat loss, for example, in double and triple glazing

HEAT

Temperature is a measure of how hot or cold an object is and it is related to the amount of heat energy the object has. In the UK, temperature is measured using the scale of **degrees Celsius (°C)**. This numerical scale is simple and is based on the way that water behaves on Earth.

As we found out, water is needed for life to survive on this planet (see page 148). Because water is vital, scientists have been studying its properties for years.

°F	°C	
110	40	a heat wave
70	20	room temperature
32	0	water Freezes
10	-10	a pleasant winter day
-10	-30	a cold winter day

A thermometer showing 0–100°C.

It is well known that water **freezes** at 0 °C, but this is only because a scientist called Anders Celsius invented the temperature scale which he based on the properties of water. Actually, he started with an 'upside down' scale in which 100 was the point at which water turned to ice! But then he found out that changing altitude (height above sea level) or pressure changed the boiling point of water. As the freezing point of water never changes it makes a better reference point, so he reversed the scale to start at 0 °C.

 Did you know?

Fact file: Anders Celsius

Born	27 November 1701
Died	25 April 1744 (aged 42)
Lived	Sweden
Nationality	Swedish
Studied at	Uppsala University
Known for	Inventing the Celsius scale
Scientific career	Astronomy, physics, mathematics, geology

HEAT AND TEMPERATURE

Heat is a form of energy and it is measured in Joules (J). Heat is often confused with temperature. Temperature is a measure of how hot or cold an object is, and it is measured in degrees Celsius. Heat and temperature are obviously closely related but they are not the same.

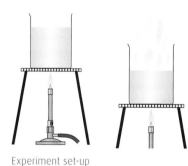

Experiment set-up

 Classroom challenge

Examining heat and temperature

Aim: To demonstrate that heat and temperature are not the same

Instructions

1 Draw a results table with three columns. Label these Temperature (°C), Beaker 1 (100 ml), Beaker 2 (200 ml). You need two rows: Starting temperature and Final temperature.
2 Collect two identical beakers.
3 Fill one with 100 ml of water and the other with 200 ml of water.
4 Place a thermometer in each beaker. Read and record the starting temperatures of the water in the beakers in your results table.
5 Heat each beaker with Bunsen burner for 5 minutes, then turn the heat off.

6　Read and record the temperature of the water in each beaker after the 5 minutes of heating.
7　Allow the beakers and tripod to cool fully before tidying away.

Questions

1　Compare the temperature rises in the beakers.
2　Can you explain what happened?

TEACHING NOTES

Visit www.brightredpublishing.co.uk for teaching notes on how to use a Bunsen burner.

The beakers were supplied with the same amount of energy because they were heated for the same amount of time. If heat and temperature are the same, we would expect the temperature rise in each beaker to be the same. Since the temperature rises in the two beakers were different, the experiment shows that temperature and heat energy are not the same thing.

Like all other forms of energy (such as light and sound) heat can transfer, or move, from one place to another. There are three different methods by which heat energy can move: **conduction**, **convection** and **radiation**

CONDUCTION, CONVECTION AND RADIATION

Heat always moves from a place of high temperature to a place of lower temperature. This is why our houses get cold in winter, even after heating them. The heat energy inside our homes moves towards the cold exterior walls and this continues until the temperatures of each region are the same.

Conduction

Conduction is the method by which heat moves in a solid substance. Particles in a solid vibrate slowly. When the atoms in a solid receive heat energy, they vibrate faster. These vibrations cause neighbouring atoms to vibrate, as some energy is passed on. This transfer of heat energy by the vibration of atoms continues throughout the solid material until the whole object becomes warmer.

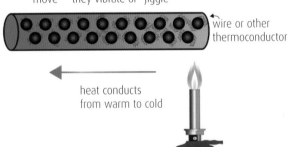

molecules in solid objects don't "move" - they vibrate or "jiggle"

wire or other thermoconductor

heat conducts from warm to cold

Conduction

Classroom challenge

Experiment to investigate conduction

Aim: To compare conductive properties of different materials

Some materials conduct better than others. This can be tested very easily.

Instructions

1 Place the ends of some different materials (wood, metal, plastic, glass) that are approximately the same size as each other into a beaker of warm water.
2 Carefully place small lumps of butter (or petroleum jelly) on to the other end of the materials.
3 Observe which lump of butter melts first.
4 Draw a table to record your findings.

Safety!

Care should be taken when handling hot water.

Which lump of butter will melt first?

TEACHING NOTES

Find instructions for this challenge by downloading the Teaching Notes from www.brightredpublishing. co.uk

Convection

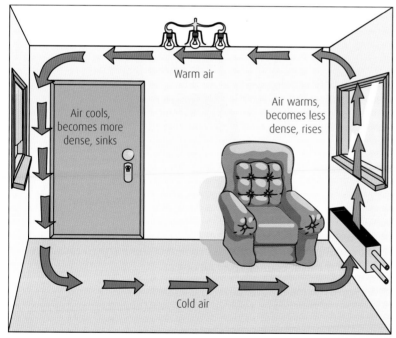

Convection in a room with a radiator

The atoms in a liquids and gases are not fixed in position, but are free to move and change position. This means very little conduction can take place, but convection can occur.

As a liquid or gas heats up, the atoms vibrate more and move further apart. This causes the hotter part of the substance to become less dense than the surrounding liquid or gas and it rises. The colder part of the substance falls into the space left by the rising substance. This colder portion is now nearer the heat source and eventually heats up, expands and rises. The particles that had previously risen have now cooled, contracted, become denser and fallen again. This is called a convection cycle.

 ## Classroom challenge

Convection experiment

Aim: To observe convection currents in water

Instructions

Find teaching notes for this challenge at www.brightredpublishing.co.uk

1 Set up the experiment as shown in the diagram.
2 Wait a short time to allow the cold water to settle, then add a single crystal of potassium manganate.
3 Gently heat the water.
4 Observe how the dye moves with the movement of the water particles as they rise and fall due to convection. Draw a diagram of your results.

Safety!

Care should be taken when handling hot water.

cold water

Potassium manganate VII crystals

small flame

Experiment set-up

Radiation

Conduction and convection both require the presence of particles to allow the transfer of heat to take place. But heat can also move in the absence of particles by the process of radiation. This is the way that heat energy from the Sun travels through 150 million kilometres of vacuum in space to Earth.

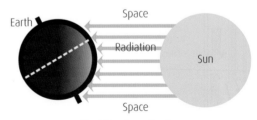
Space
Earth
Radiation
Sun
Space
Radiation from the Sun

Heat is emitted as **infrared radiation**.
Infrared is a type of **electromagnetic (EM)** radiation and, like all EM radiation, it travels at the speed of light in a vacuum. Infrared cameras can detect this infrared radiation, giving us information about the heat emitted from an object.

Radiation and convection are the main ways that we heat our homes.

Classroom challenge

Investigating radiation

Aim: To compare radiation of heat energy from two different surfaces

Instructions

1 Fill two identically sized containers, one blackened and the other silvered, with hot or warm water.
2 Record the temperature fall in both containers every minute for 10 minutes and notice the overall temperature changes.
3 Make a line graph of your table of results
4 What happened? Find out why.
5 Using your graph and your **predicting skills** determine the temperature fall after 12 minutes for both containers.

Safety!

Care should be taken when handling hot water. Allow any hot water to cool down before attempting to move the container.

CONDUCTORS AND INSULATORS

Not all materials are equally capable of transferring heat energy by conduction. Each material has a **thermal conductivity**, which is a measure of how easily that material will allow heat to transfer through it.

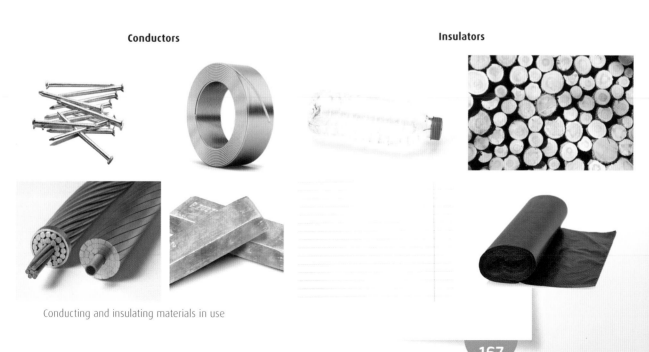

Conducting and insulating materials in use

Materials with a high thermal conductivity are known as conductors; these are good at allowing heat to move through them. Good conductors are typically metals like iron or copper. They are often used to make objects like cooking pots.

Materials with a low thermal conductivity are known as insulators; these are good at opposing the movement of heat through them. Insulators tend to be non-metallic substances, such as rubber or plastic, and are used for objects that stop or reduce heat flow.

 ## Classroom challenge

Head to the Bright Red website and download the Homework Helpers bundle for an additional activity on heat and heat transfer!

Materials, properties and uses

Instructions

1 Use your **processing skills** and **researching skills** to make a table of common materials.

2 Indicate whether they each one is a heat conductor or heat insulator.
3 Describe a use for each material that is related to its properties.

Questions

1 Name the process by which heat energy is able to move inside a solid object. Describe how this occurs.
2 In materials of which states of matter does heat movement by conduction occur?
3 What kind of EM radiation is emitted when heat movement by radiation occurs?
4 List three heat conductors and three heat insulator materials. Explain where each of these materials are used according to these properties.

EARTH'S MATERIALS

I can use the materials around me to help me survive. The ground I walk on contains lots of different elements and compounds, some of which will be very helpful to me as I rebuild my life.

*When people first discovered the Earth's useful resources, they used them without really considering the impact of their actions. For example, humans have burned irreplaceable **fossil fuels** that took millions of years to form to provide instant electricity.*

Don't get me wrong, I would love to be able to turn on the TV, flick a light switch or cook in an oven, instead of collecting firewood for heat and light. Perhaps I will be able to use alternative sources of power.

The outcomes and experiences for this chapter are:

❝I can design and carry out practical activities to develop my understanding of chemical reactions involving the Earth's materials. I can explain how we apply knowledge of these reactions in practical ways.❞ SCN 3–19b

What's coming up?

- Describing chemical reactions involving the Earth's materials, for example, combustion of fossil fuels, carbonate rocks reacting with acid and the formation and impact of acid rain

FOSSIL FUELS

Fossil fuels started forming hundreds of millions of years ago. Living materials, both plant and animal, died and fell to the ground. Over time, mud and rocks piled on top of them, putting them under intense pressure. The breakdown of the dead material also created heat. With heat and pressure, dead plant material formed coal and dead animal life formed oil.

Humans mined for the coal and drilled for the oil, bringing these to the Earth's surface again. We discovered that, when burned, fossil fuels release energy. This energy can be used to make electricity.

Did you know?

Mining in Scotland

Coal has been mined in Scotland for over 200 years. In the early nineteenth century, almost all coal was burned for heat in the homes and businesses of the surrounding area.

This coal would have been extracted manually in underground mines or 'pits' using picks and shovels. It was not uncommon for children as young as six to join the workforce in dangerous and unsafe conditions.

By 1842 the government had raised the minimum age for mine workers to 10 years, and then later to 13. It wasn't until the 1880s that mining with machinery became more common and surface mining was developed.

By the mid-twentieth century, coal was being used to produce electricity in power stations. In order to meet demand for coal, the mining industry became heavily industrialised. In 1955, 700 000 Scots were employed in mining. Massive 'super-pits' opened in Fife and elsewhere to extract large reserves of coal that became accessible through new mining technologies and techniques.

Today we understand that burning fossil fuels comes at a cost to the environment (page 171). Governments around the world are trying to limit the use of coal, oil and gas as fuels.

Scotland is lucky to have an abundance of alternative energy options, such as water, wind and wave power. We are leading the world in developing technologies that harness naturally occurring energy sources.

 How does that work?

Generating electricity

Electricity is primarily made by burning material to heat water. The steam that is made is used to turn a turbine. When the turbine is turning, it turns a generator which produces electricity.

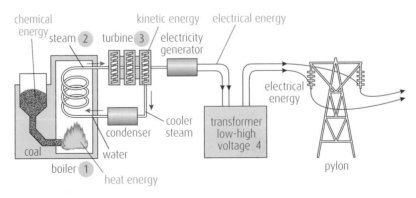

Key:
1 Water is heated by burning fuel
2 Steam turns a turbine
3 A generator turns
4 Electricity is generated and distributed

BURNING FOSSIL FUELS

In order to rebuild we need to start generating electricity; the power went off when the bombs dropped. Power stations were automatically shut down because they were unsafe and there weren't enough people to run them.

One of the disadvantages of burning fossil fuels is the pollution it causes. When fossil fuels are burned they create carbon dioxide, a greenhouse gas (see page 85) and water.

Combustion

Fuel (plant material) + $O_2 \rightarrow CO_2 + H_2O$ + Energy

Word equation for combustion of fossil fuels

 ## Classroom challenge

Burning hydrocarbon demonstration

Aim: To investigate the products of hydrocarbon combustion.

Instructions

1 Your teacher will set up the experiment shown in the diagram. Smoke from fuel combustion is caught by the funnel and is pulled along the system by a water pump.
2 Observe changes in the cobalt chloride paper and limewater and deduce what products are made when a fuel is burned.

 **TEACHING NOTES**

Visit www.brightredpublishing. co.uk for class notes on identifying the products of combustion.

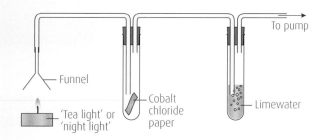

To pump

Funnel

'Tea light' or 'night light'

Cobalt chloride paper

Limewater

The cobalt chloride paper turns pink to show that water has been produced (this colour change happens faster if the test tube is placed into a beaker of ice water). Bubbles are produced in the limewater, which turns milky. This demonstrates that carbon dioxide is also made.

Acid rain

Burning fuels creates pollutants which are released into the air. We already know about the effects of increased levels of carbon dioxide in the air.

Sulfur dioxide and nitrogen dioxide are produced when impurities in fossil fuels burn. These two gases mix with the water in the atmosphere to create **acid rain.** As you can imagine, rain that is acidic is not good for the environment.

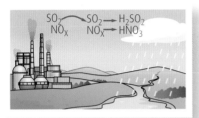  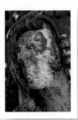 

The effects of acid rain can be devastating to living things, both plants and animals, as well as certain types of stonework and buildings

 Classroom challenge

Researching the effects of acid rain

Instructions

1 Choose one of the following effects of acid rain and use your **researching skills** to find out more about it: deforestation, erosion of stone or death of aquatic life.
2 Present your research in the form of an informational leaflet. It should be tri-fold and double-sided in format. Follow this page plan:

- Page 1 – Produce a colourful front cover that clearly shows what the rest of the leaflet is about
- Page 2 – Outline the problem have you chosen to research
- Page 3 – Describe the issues this causes
- Page 4 – Say why this is a problem
- Page 5 – Suggest what we can do about it
- Page 6 – Give your sources of information (references).

There is more practice on this topic on the Bright Red website: download the Homework Helpers and complete the activity on reactions of earth materials.

RENEWABLE ENERGY

*It is very important to remember that fossil fuels are **finite** – they will run out. Before the war, the world mainly produced its electrical energy using **non-renewable fuels**.*

We were already starting to run out of them before the war, so we really can't rely on using them to rebuild, now that we need to start again. Perhaps we should see this terrible time as an opportunity to do better making energy in the future.

The outcomes and experiences for this chapter are:

I can discuss the benefits and potential problems of renewable energy sources because I have investigated them and taken part in practical activities to harness them. SCN 3–04b

What's coming up?

- Presenting research findings on the advantages and disadvantages associated with the use of renewable energy sources and their impact on society, demonstrating an informed view based on evidence

GENERATING ENERGY

Non-renewable forms of energy, such as coal, oil and gas, are running out.

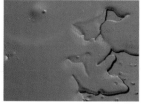

Fossil fuels

Non-renewable forms of energy

Nuclear power

Radioactive material, such as uranium, can be used as a fuel in nuclear power stations to produce huge amounts of electricity. Uranium is not burned like a fossil fuel. Instead, controlled nuclear reactions occur inside a reactor. The energy that is released is used to heat water and the steam is used to drive turbines. Carbon dioxide is not produced, but nuclear waste is a problem. These very hazardous radioactive chemicals have to be stored safely – potentially for hundreds of years.

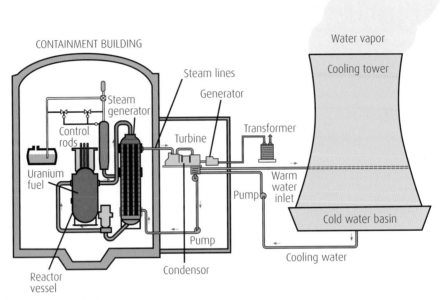

CONTAINMENT BUILDING

Steam lines

Steam generator

Generator

Control rods

Transformer

Turbine

Uranium fuel

Water vapor

Cooling tower

Warm water inlet

Pump

Cold water basin

Pump

Condensor

Reactor vessel

Cooling water

Nuclear reactions can be harnessed to generate power

 ## Classroom challenge

Fossil fuel reserves

Non-renewable energy sources are all finite. This means one day we will run out of these resources.

Instructions

Using your library or the internet, find out how long it will be before fossil fuels will run out, according to experts.

 **DON'T FORGET**

Make sure to use a reliable source for your information.

RENEWABLE FORMS OF ENERGY

Renewable forms of energy produce electricity from sources of energy that will not run out. Examples are light and heat energy from the Sun and kinetic energy from moving air or water. Generally speaking, renewable methods of producing energy are clean, cause very little or no pollution and have minimal impact on our environment. However, the main drawback tends to be that these methods are less efficient and produce much smaller amounts of electricity compared to nuclear and fossil fuels.

Solar cells

Solar cells (or solar panels) produce electrical energy from light energy that comes from the Sun. This is very useful during the day, producing electricity that can be used to power household appliances or electronic road signs. During the night, however they are unable to produce any energy and we have to depend on other energy sources for our electricity. This problem is being worked on and scientists are

Solar cells on a roof

researching ways that we can store the energy solar panels make during the day so that we could use it overnight too.

Wind turbines

Wind turbines are able to produce electrical energy from the wind (kinetic energy of the air). Moving air currents push on the rotor blades, causing them to spin and rotating a generator, which produces electricity. A single turbine only produces a small amount of electrical energy, so they are often grouped in wind farms. These are collections of large wind turbines that, combined, can produce large amounts of electrical energy.

Wind turbines

Some people complain of the impact that vast numbers of these large mechanical structures have on the beauty of our countryside, but they do produce pollution-free electricity.

Water and wave power

Hydroelectric power stations and wave turbines are able to produce electrical energy from moving water. Hydroelectric power stations are often built across fast-flowing rivers or between two reservoirs (artificial lakes for water storage) with a difference in height. Both methods use the energy of fast-flowing water to turn turbines that turn electric generators to produce electricity.

A hydroelectric power station

The environmental impact is kept to a minimum as water is not used up; un polluted water is fed back into the river or reservoir. A specific landscape is required for a hydroelectric power station and flooding may be involved in creation of reservoirs.

Biomass

Biomass (organic material, such as trees or waste products) is burned like a fossil fuel to produce heat and then electrical energy. This is a controversial form of renewable energy as it produces carbon dioxide and other pollutants. However, it uses up waste products that would be disposed of anyway.

It is a renewable source of energy because, when wood is used, plant stocks can be replaced. Wood is still the most common form of biomass; in some developing countries it is the only available source of energy.

The type of biomass used in particular areas depends on the local industries. Scotland, where forestry is a traditional industry, uses wood. However, rice husks are much more available in South Asia, so that is what is used there.

 ## Classroom challenge

Advantages and disadvantages of renewable technologies

Instructions

Devise a table to show an advantage and a disadvantage for each kind of renewable energy source.

Questions

1 Explain the difference between non-renewable and renewable sources of energy.
2 Using your **processing skills** make a table giving examples of renewable and non-renewable sources of energy.
3 What are the advantages and disadvantages of using fossil fuels to produce electricity?
4 Which renewable forms of energy are used in Scotland? Why do we use these rather than other renewable forms of energy?

DON'T FORGET

If you get stuck, look through your book; there is some useful information in Impact! which could help you.

There is an additional homework practice activity on renewable energy on the Bright Red website. Just visit www.brightredpublishing.co.uk and download the Homework Helpers to get started.

CHEMICAL CELLS

*There are limited options for energy generation at the moment. I haven't managed to salvage any solar panels or wind turbines yet, so I'm going to start small scale and try to make my own **chemical cell**, using elements and compounds that are readily available on Earth.*

The outcomes and experiences for this chapter are:

I can help to design simple chemical cells and use them to investigate the factors which affect the voltage produced. SCN 3–10a

What's coming up?

- Investigating how to produce electricity using different metals and electrolytes
- Producing a full lab report for an investigation into the voltage produced when altering a range of factors

WHAT IS A CHEMICAL CELL?

We've all seen and used chemical cells before. They are very simple batteries. Batteries turn chemical energy into electrical energy. Electrical energy is, very simply, the movement of charged particles – called electrons – through wires to provide power.

Classroom challenge

Pros and cons of electrical sources

Instructions

1 In pairs, list all the times you use electricity in your everyday life.
2 Now, go through that list and identify all the electrical items that use batteries.
3 Use a table like Table 22 to set out the pros and cons of using batteries and mains electricity. You could use the internet to help you find answers.

Table 22 Advantages and disadvantages of mains and batteries as sources of electricity

Pros of using batteries	Cons of using batteries	Pros of using mains electricity	Cons of using mains electricity

A battery works by moving charged particles from the negative side of the battery to the positive side. It moves the charges through an **electrolyte**, which is a liquid or gel containing ions.

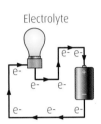

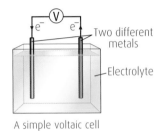

A simple voltaic cell

A chemical cell is similar. It allows the movement of charged particles from one metal to another to create a **voltage**. This voltage can be measured easily using a voltmeter.

 Classroom challenge

Finding out about chemical cells

Questions

1   Describe what is meant by the term *chemical cell*.
2   Give five examples of devices you have in your home that require cells (or batteries) to operate.
3   Describe how a chemical cell produces a voltage.
4   Different materials can be used to build a chemical cell. Use the internet or library to find out (a) what materials are used to make a mobile phone battery and (b) what materials are used in a common AA battery.

 Classroom challenge

Chemical cell experiment

Aim: To make your own chemical cell to produce a voltage

Equipment

- Variety of metal strips (including copper)
- Salty water
- Wires with crocodile clips
- Voltmeter

Instructions

1   Attach the wires to the voltmeter.
2   Connect a copper strip to one of the wires with a crocodile clip.
3   Attach another strip of copper to the other wire.
4   Place the copper strips into a small beaker half filled with salty water.

5   Take a reading from the voltmeter and record this into a results table like Table 23.
6   Remove one of the copper strips and replace it with one of the other metal strips.
7   Place the metal strips into the salty water and record the result.
8   Repeat this with all the available metals until your results table is complete.

Table 23 Example results table

Materials Tested	Voltage (v)
Magnesium	−2.35
Zinc	−0.76
Iron	−0.45
Tin	−0.15
Hydrogen	+0.00
Copper	+0.34
Silver	+0.80

Questions

1   Use your processing skills to make a graph of the results given in Table 23, making sure to choose the correct format.
2   Analyse your graph to determine which metal produces the highest voltage?
3   Which metal produces the lowest voltage?
4   If you had to use these results to help you decide which metals to use to make yourself a torch, which would you choose and why?
5   **Analyse** the table of results: which one of the 'Materials Tested' in Table 23 is the odd one out? Why? Find out why this chemical is included in list like that given in Table 23.

Electrolyte investigation

Aim: To investigate the effect of electrolyte on voltage produced

Instructions

You can use the experimental set-up from the challenge on page 178 to investigate different factors, by creating different independent and dependant variables.

1   Look at the aim of this investigation and plan what you are going to do.
2   Check your plan with your teacher before carrying out your investigation.
3   Using the lab-report template (see page 30), you should write a report of your investigation.
4   Using information on page 16 for reference, write aims for experiments with the following variables:

   1   independent – type of electrolyte used
       dependant – voltage produced
   2   independent – distance between electrodes
       dependant – voltage produced
   3   independent – surface area of electrodes
       dependant – voltage produced

Find teaching notes for this challenge at www.brightredpublishing.co.uk

There is more practice on chemical cells on the Bright Red website! Visit www.brightredpublishing.co.uk and download the Homework Helpers to strengthen your knowledge.

CIRCUITS

Now that I have figured out how to produce a voltage, I am looking at storing that voltage in the form of batteries. If I can build my own batteries, I will have power any time I need it.

I am going to think about how to use the stored energy in a meaningful way. There is absolutely no point to having stores of electricity and not knowing how to use them!

The outcomes and experiences for this chapter are:

I can design a circuit to show the advantages of parallel circuits in an everyday application because I have measured the current and voltage in series and parallel circuits. SCN 3–09a

 What's coming up?

- Applying knowledge from practical investigations to describe the similarities and differences between series and parallel circuits, and explain the advantages of parallel circuits in an everyday application

HARNESSING ELECTRICAL ENERGY

Circuits and circuit symbols

A **circuit** is a conducting pathway that electrical energy travels through. Electricity is able to travel through conducting materials, generally metals, very easily. Electrical **insulating** materials such as plastic or wood do not allow electrical energy to pass through them.

Conductors   **Insulators**

salt water

copper

plastic

wood glass

steel

gold

paper

rubber

Conducting and insulating objects

Circuits direct electrical energy around a pathway to make a device work.

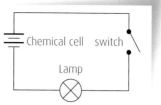

Electrical energy is given out by the chemical cell. Opening and closing the switch controls the flow of the electrical energy. A closed switch creates a continuous path between both sides of the battery, allowing electrical energy to flow. It flows around the circuit and through the lamp. Electrical energy is changed into light energy inside the lamp.

A circuit diagram using symbols to represent components

Opening the switch creates an **open circuit** with a gap through which electrical energy cannot flow. This stops any current flowing and the lamp does not light.

Series circuits

A **series circuit** is the simplest of circuit designs. A series circuit has one continuous path for the electrical energy to travel through.

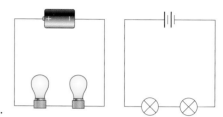

 ## Classroom challenge

Building series circuits

Equipment

Find teaching notes for this challenge at www.brightredpublishing.co.uk

- A battery
- Wires
- Three lamps

Instructions

Build the circuit as shown in the diagram above. Create a circuit with one, two and then three lamps.

Questions

1   What do you notice about the brightness of the lamps as you add more lamps into the circuit?
2   Find out what happens to the other lamps when one lamp is removed (and not replaced) or is broken?

In a series circuit, the lamps 'share' the available energy between them. As the number of lamps increase, the energy is shared further and the brightness of each reduces.

When one of the lamps breaks or is removed, the continuous path is broken – a gap has been made creating open circuit and the electrical energy will not flow. None of the lamps will light.

Parallel circuits

A parallel circuit is a circuit design with more than one path for the electrical energy to follow.

Classroom challenge

Building parallel circuits

Instructions

1 Build the circuit shown in the diagram.
2 Repeat the same steps as with the series circuit
   challenge on page 181.

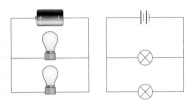

Questions

1 What do you notice about the brightness of the
   bulbs this time?
2 What happens when you remove one of the bulbs?

TEACHING NOTES

Find teaching notes for
this challenge at www.
brightredpublishing.co.uk

Each branch of the parallel circuit receives the full amount of electrical energy from
the power supply (battery), meaning the bulbs do not share the energy and are brighter.
When one lamp is removed or broken, the gap in the circuit only occurs in that branch.
The other branches are still complete, meaning those lamps will still light.

Advantages of parallel circuits

Parallel circuits are often used instead of series circuits, because all parts of the circuit
receive the same amount of energy and because an interruption in one part of the circuit
does not stop the current flowing completely.

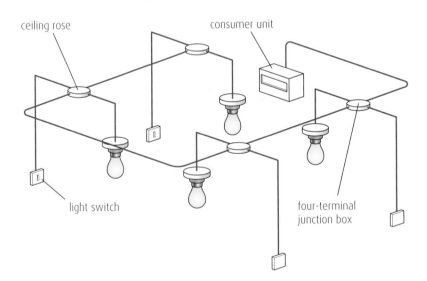

ceiling rose

consumer unit

light switch

four-terminal
junction box

Lights in a house are wired together in a type of parallel circuit called a **ring circuit**,
rather than using a series circuit.

In a parallel circuit, each of the lamps can be turned on separately, as the lamp and
corresponding switch are on their own branch of the parallel circuit. If one of the lamps

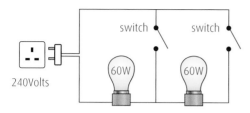

240Volts

were to become faulty or to break, the other lamps in the circuit would still work. Only the branch with the faulty lamp will have an open circuit.

Also, when each lamp is on its own branch of the parallel circuit, all of the lamps receive the full voltage from the power supply. This means that each lamp operates at full brightness.

Classroom challenge

Drawing circuits

Questions

1. Draw a circuit diagram for a parallel circuit with a battery, three bulbs and a switch for each bulb.
2. Explain how your circuit works.
3. A switch is connected to a battery and two lamps. When the switch is pressed both lamps come on. Draw this as a series circuit and as a parallel circuit.
4. Give two advantages of a parallel circuit over a series circuit.
5. Give a real-life example of where a parallel circuit is used rather than a series circuit. Draw the circuit diagram to help explain.

> Visit the Bright Red website and download the Homework Helpers for an additional activity on circuits.

CHEMICAL REACTIONS

Once I have a way of adding energy (be that heat, light or electrical energy) to different elements from the Periodic Table, I can start to experiment with making compounds that would be more useful for me in my current position.

The outcomes and experiences for this chapter are:

I can identify indicators of chemical reactions having occurred. I can describe ways of controlling the rate of reactions and can relate my findings to the world around me. SCN 3–19a

I can describe examples of how the properties of compounds are different from their constituent elements. SCN 3–15b

What's coming up?

- Identifying indicators of chemical reactions such as colour change, precipitate formation, release of gas, and/or a detectable energy change
- Finding the relationship between particle size, concentration, temperature, and catalysts and the rate of a reaction
- Explaining how catalysts, including enzymes, can be used to speed up chemical reactions, and providing at least two everyday examples of reactions involving a catalyst
- Constructing names of two-element compounds which are derived from the names of the elements from which it is formed, with a suffix of-ide
- Constructing word equations for simple reactions, for example, carbon reacting with oxygen: carbon + oxygen → carbon dioxide

MAKING COMPOUNDS

Compounds are made by chemical reactions. In all chemical reactions at least one new substance is formed. This happens when elements (listed in Periodic Table) combine, or bond, to make something new. One of the most important chemical reactions on Earth is the reaction between two colourless, odourless gases, oxygen (O_2) and hydrogen (H_2), to make water (H_2O):

oxygen + hydrogen → water

Oxygen and hydrogen don't just join together easily. If they did, there would be no oxygen or hydrogen gas left. There is a very specific set of circumstances that have to happen to allow this chemical reaction to take place.

A reaction can be very quick or very slow depending on what is being made.

How does that work?

Comparing chemical reactions

Every reaction that takes place on our Earth is different. Every reaction has its own speed due to the way the particles involved are moving.

- Some examples of fast reactions are matches catching fire, glowsticks glowing and an egg being fried.
- Some slow reactions are rusting and the chemical reactions that weather rocks.

Some examples of slow reactions are metals rusting and chemical weathering.

 Classroom challenge

Reaction speed

Instructions

The pictures show different reactions that have different speeds. Using your knowledge of everyday chemical reactions, choose five different reactions and organise them from slowest to fastest.

If necessary, use the internet to help you look up different examples of everyday chemical reactions.

CATALYSTS

Sometimes it is useful to change the speed at which a reaction happens. There is no point in making a new substance so quickly you cannot collect it, and there is also no point in making a substance so slowly that you cannot use it. Catalysts allow us to change the speed at which some reactions occur.

 ## Classroom challenge

Catalyst experiment

Aim: To investigate a catalyst

Hydrogen peroxide is made of the same chemicals as water, hydrogen and oxygen, but in a different ratio. Water has two hydrogens and one oxygen joined together (H_2O), while hydrogen peroxide has two of each (H_2O_2). This extra oxygen makes a huge difference chemically. Water is safe to drink; hydrogen peroxide definitely is not! It is a bleaching agent.

Catalysts are very specific in how they work. Manganese dioxide is a catalyst that only works to speed up the breakdown of hydrogen peroxide into safe substances – oxygen and water.

Equipment

- Two test tubes
- Water
- Hydrogen peroxide
- A small spatula
- Manganese dioxide

TEACHING NOTES

Access notes on conducting an experiment on hydrogen peroxide decomposition at www.brightredpublishing.co.uk

Instructions

1 Take two labelled test tubes and half-fill one with water and one with hydrogen peroxide.
2 Make an observation of each liquid and record what they look like in your table of results.
3 Add a small spatula of manganese dioxide into both test tubes.
4 Make another observation of both test tubes and record what they look like into your results table.

All chemical reactions require energy to get going, so the first thing that we can do to make a reaction go faster is add a special chemical that helps get the reaction started. This chemical is called a **catalyst**. Catalysts speed up reactions but they do not get used up. They are still present at the end of the reaction and they remain unchanged.

Practise on what you've learnt about catalysts by completing the exercise in the Homework Helpers.

You have **biological catalysts** in your body called **enzymes**. You have an enzyme in the saliva (spit) in your mouth. This enzyme speeds up the process of digestion (see page 108).

We use **chemical catalysts** in industry. They can speed up production of ammonia for fertilisers (see page 81) and can break down chemicals into their elements.

Catalysts are specific to particular reactions. They do not work with every reaction.

OTHER FACTORS THAT AFFECT THE REACTION RATE

There are other simple changes we can make to change the speed, or **rate of reaction**, which don't involve catalysts. Chances are you do some of these things every day to speed up the chemical reactions you carry out.

Particle size

Changing the size of the surfaces of the chemicals that are reacting is an easy way to help speed up the reaction. Let's look at an everyday chemical reaction: cooking.

You know that if you chop potatoes into small chunks they will cook faster than if you leave them whole. Why does this happen?

The smaller the pieces of potato, the larger the **surface area.**

The greater the surface area that is available for a chemical reaction to take place, the less time it will take to complete the change into the new substance; in this case from raw potato to cooked potato.

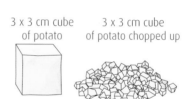

3 x 3 cm cube of potato   3 x 3 cm cube of potato chopped up

Concentration

Concentration also has an effect on the rate of a reaction. If you increase the concentration of a chemical in a reaction, the reaction will speed up.

Temperature

Temperature also affects reaction rate. Temperature is a measure of the energy in a chemical; the higher the temperature, the higher the energy and the lower the temperature, the lower the energy.

melting →   boiling →

solid   liquid   gas

Particles of water in all three states of matter

When water is in the solid state (ice) all of the particles have low energy and are arranged in a neat and rigid pattern. They stay in place, vibrating and rotating slowly, but not moving away from each other. Steam is the gas form of water. These particles have a higher temperature and higher energy, and they move quickly.

A chemical at a higher temperature has more thermal energy, so its particles can move more. When a particle can move it is more likely to bump into another chemical so a chemical reaction can take place.

Reactions are like bumper cars: if a chemical reaction takes place when two cars hit each other head on at full speed, the reaction overall will happen faster when all the cars are going at full speed all the time!

 Classroom challenge

Reaction rates can be calculated using experimental data which is displayed in the form of a table of results.

Download the Homework Helpers from the Bright Red website and find an extra activity on rates of reaction.

1   Use your **predicting skills** to fill in the missing value:

Time (s)	Gas produced (cm³)
0	0
5	10
10	20
15	
20	40

2   Using the information from the table of results draw a graph. Make sure you sure an appropriate scale.
3   Extend the line of your graph and use your **predicting skills** to state what the volume of gas produced would be at 25 seconds.

SPOTTING SIGNS OF A REACTION

It's important for me to understand how to speed up chemical reactions. It could be the difference between eating and going hungry. Although there is not much point in understanding how to make a reaction faster if I don't know when a reaction has actually happened.

There are signs of a chemical reaction that are useful to know.

 ## Classroom challenge

Experimental tests

Example experiments include burning methane, adding chalk to acid, reacting an acid and an alkali, and mixing potassium iodide and lead nitrate.

Instructions

1 Using the chemicals and directions your teacher has provided, carry out a number of small experiments.
2 What are the signs that a new substance has been formed?
3 Use a table like Table 24 to record your results.

Table 24 Observations of chemical reactions

Chemical reaction	Observations
Burning methane	Change in temperature, heat and light given off

 **TEACHING NOTES**

Download risk assessment forms at www.brightredpublishing. co.uk

Knowing the signs of a chemical reaction makes it easier to spot when a reaction has taken place. Not all chemical reactions are easy to spot, but there are four things to look for:

- a change in temperature
- formation of a precipitate (a solid that forms when two liquids are added together)
- formation of a gas (this can be invisible or may be seen as bubbles in a liquid)
- a colour change

Which, if any of these four changes takes place, depends on the reaction.

One of the more difficult signs to detect is a change (increase or decrease) in temperature.

All reactions *require* energy to break down the starting chemicals into reacting parts and all reactions *release* energy when they make new chemicals. Whether reaction mixtures heat up or cool down depends on the balance between these two phases.

Formation of a precipitate is a clear sign that a reaction has taken place. When two liquids are added together and a solid forms it is obvious that a new substance has been created, although the solid may not be the only new thing made. Any liquid that is left after the solid has formed is likely to contain new chemicals too!

One of the signs of a chemical reaction can be seen and heard! When two chemicals are put together and bubbles form, you may actually hear fizzing.

A colour change is an obvious sign that a new substance has formed. A simple example of this is found in cooking; the cooking reaction has happened when meat is no longer red.

You need to be careful when interpreting this sign. Sometimes when two chemicals are put together, they will mix but not react. If the starting chemicals are different colours, mixing them may create a new combined colour but a chemical reaction has not occurred.

When chemical reactions form new substances, these must have new names. The names need to reflect what the compounds are made from, but must clearly show that the new chemicals are different from the starting chemicals.

Naming compounds

There are some simple rules for naming compounds:

- The metal element is named first, followed by the non-metal.
- The second element in the name has a special ending, for example –ide.

There is more practice on compounds and chemical reactions in the Homework Helpers.

Consider this reaction:

Magnesium + Oxygen → Magnesium oxide

The start of the name of the new chemical shows us what substances it is made from: magnesium and oxygen. Magnesium is the metal, so that part of the name comes first. Oxygen is the non-metal, so that part of the name comes second. The ending of 'Oxygen' is changed to 'oxide' to show that the two atoms have joined together and a new chemical has been made.

These rules are the same for naming all compounds with only two elements.

There is another rule for compounds that are made of three elements where the third element is Oxygen.

- If there are two elements and also Oxygen, the ending is changed to –ate.

For example:

Sodium + Carbon + Oxygen → Sodium carbonate

Classroom challenge

Your turn

Questions

Following the three simple rules noted on page 190, use your **processing skills** to deduce the names of the new substances formed when these elements join together chemically:

1　Lithium and Bromine
2　Potassium and Iodine
3　Caesium and Fluorine
4　Magnesium and Oxygen
5　Sodium and Chlorine
6　Calcium, Oxygen and Phosphorus
7　Sulfur, Calcium and Oxygen.

Now work out the elements that made the following compounds:

8　Aluminium bromide
9　Strontium iodide
10　Calcium carbonate
11　Beryllium phosphide
12　Boron fluoride.

Find an additional activity on the signs of a chemical reaction in our Homework Helpers at www.brightredpublishing.co.uk

ELECTROMAGNETIC RADIATION

I've managed to figure out the basics; I think I'm going to survive. But I'm not sure I can do it alone. I need to find other people to help me rebuild.

To find people, I need to communicate; I need to understand how methods of communication work. I need to get to grips with the electromagnetic spectrum.

The outcomes and experiences for this chapter are:

I can describe a selected application, discussing the advantages and limitations because I have explored radiations beyond the visible. SCN 3–11b

I can explain how light can be used in a variety of applications because I have explored the refraction of light through different materials, lenses and prisms. SCN3.11a

What's coming up?

- Describing the electromagnetic spectrum as a family of waves including gamma rays, X-rays, ultraviolet, visible light, infrared, microwaves, television and radio waves
- Researching at least one application of an electromagnetic wave beyond the visible in everyday life, giving advantages and limitations of that application
- Exploring the way that visible light refracts through different materials, lenses and prisms

UNDERSTANDING RADIATION

The electromagnetic spectrum

The **electromagnetic (EM) spectrum** is a range of types of radiation that consist of electric and magnetic waves, all travelling at the speed of light. There are broadly seven types of EM radiation that range from very low to very high energy waves:

- gamma rays
- X-rays
- ultraviolet rays
- visible light
- infrared waves
- microwaves
- radio waves

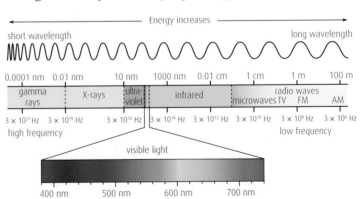

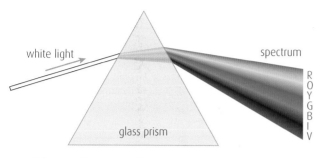

white light

spectrum

R
O
Y
G
B
I
V

glass prism

Visible light waves are the band of EM waves that we can see. Each wavelength of light produces a slightly different colour, from violet at one end of the spectrum to red at the other, through all the colours of the rainbow in between.

These colours can be seen when passing a beam of white light through a prism. The prism changes the speed of the coloured lights that make up the white light and each wavelength exits the prism in a slightly different direction, causing the colours to be seen separately.

As in the case of the white light and glass prism, light always changes its path when it passes through different materials. Light waves travel in a straight line until they meet a material with a different density, which changes its speed. The change in speed causes the light to change direction, which is called **refraction**.

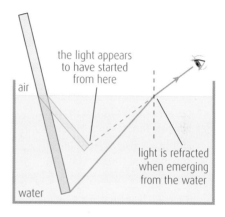

the light appears to have started from here

air

water

light is refracted when emerging from the water

Classroom challenge

Find an additional activity on refraction by downloading the Homework Helpers bundle at www.brightredpublishing.co.uk

Bending pencils

Can you bend a pencil without touching it? Using the idea of refraction you can!

Equipment

- A glass
- Water
- A pencil

Instructions

1 Half-fill a glass with water and place a pencil in it, leaning it against the side.
2 Look at the pencil through the side of the glass. It will look bent.
3 Remove the pencil from the water to make sure it is still straight.

So, why did the pencil look bent when it was in the water? Light rays change direction before they reach your eyes as they move from the water to the glass to the air. This makes the pencil look bent and the point of the pencil appears halfway up the glass.

Did you know?

Sight correction

The refraction of light through different materials helps many people in their daily lives. People who need glasses or contact lenses are said to have a 'refractive error', which means that light doesn't hit the correct part of the eye and the person's vision is blurry. We can use glass and plastic lenses to bend the light in the correct way, so that it does hit the right part (the retina) of the eye and the person can see more clearly.

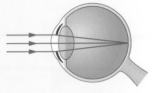

Light is focusing correctly onto the retina, so we see things clearly. ✓

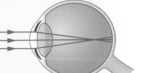

Light is not focusing correctly onto the retina, so things appear blurry. ✗

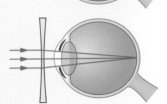

Glasses help to focus light to the correct place so that we can see clearly. ✓

This is also the same science that make light microscopes work (see page 104).

Uses of radiation

Sections of the EM spectrum have been used to develop various different technologies that help in our everyday lives. **Radio waves** have the lowest energy in the EM spectrum, but in many ways they have had the greatest impact on our lives.

Radio waves have been used for well over 100 years to carry audio signals as a form of long range communication. Radio waves are used for simple land-based radio communication and also for sophisticated satellite communication that transfers data between Earth and space.

Walkie-talkies use radio waves to carry sound signals over ranges of up to 50 km. A person speaks into the walkie-talkie's microphone and radio waves carry the sound signal in all directions. Another person with a walkie-talkie can receive the signals and hear the message through their walkie-talkie's loudspeaker.

Radio waves are good at bending (diffracting) around obstacles, so messages can still be sent and received in hilly or built up areas although the maximum range will be reduced.

Microwaves are between infrared and radio waves, in terms of the energy they carry. Microwaves are used microwave ovens to heat food. The microwaves vibrate water molecules in the food, causing heat from the frictional forces of moving particles to be produced. Microwaves can also be used for communication; Bluetooth works on the same frequency as microwaves.

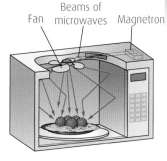

Beams of
Fan microwaves Magnetron

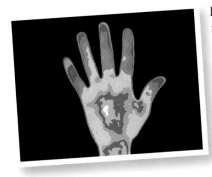

Infrared waves are emitted from objects that contain heat energy. We can use special cameras to detect this infrared radiation and use it to determine the temperature of objects. In an image like the one above the difference in temperature in a human hand is shown by giving it a visible light colour. White is the hottest part of the hand and purple is the coldest. This means that we can see that the palm of the hand is the hottest and the tips of the fingers are the coldest.

Ultraviolet waves are given out by the Sun. Some of these make it through our atmosphere to the surface. This radiation can damage our skin cells and cause skin cancer if we are unprotected. There are a number of ways you can protect yourself from harmful UV rays the most effective way it to stay covered or sheltered. Wear sunglasses and hats and light cover up's. You should also wear sun cream to protect your exposed skin, as the sun cream will stop the harmful rays from reaching your cells and causing the damage that causes cancerous changes.

OUR SUN IN UV

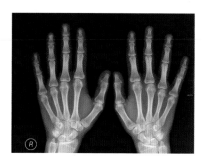

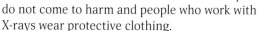

X-rays are the second highest energy waves in the EM spectrum. Since they carry such large amounts of energy, they can be harmful to living cells that are overexposed by causing cancerous changes. X-rays have been used by the medical profession for many years to obtain images of our bones and organs. Use of medical X-rays is limited so patients do not come to harm and people who work with X-rays wear protective clothing.

Gamma rays are the highest energy band on the electromagnetic spectrum and are harmful to living cells.The energy these rays deliver to living cells

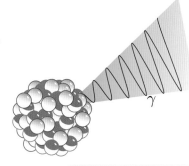

can cause cancerous changes which can lead to cancer. Gamma rays are associated with high energy nuclear reactions and may form part of the fallout after a nuclear explosion. Gamma rays are used under controlled conditions to deliberately kill living cancer cells in a treatment called **radiotherapy.** In this instance the rest of your body would be protected by a lead apron as lead can stop gamma radiation from reaching the cells and causing further damage.

 Classroom challenge

Revising EM radiation

Questions

Use the information in this section and your **selecting skills** to complete the following tasks.

1 Make a table that lists each of the types of EM radiation in order of highest to lowest energy.
2 Add a column to your table to give a use for each type of EM radiation.
3 Which types of EM radiation damage the cells of living things? Explain how we can protect ourselves from each kind of radiation.
4 Telecommunications is communication over long distances. Which types of EM radiation are specifically used in these technologies? Give examples of where they are used.
5 Using your predicting skills fill in the missing value from the table.

Electromagnetic Radiation	Frequency (Hz)
Radio waves	10^4
Microwaves	10^8
Infrared radiation	10^{12}
Visible light	10^{15}
Ultraviolet	
X-rays	10^{18}
Gamma rays	10^{20}

Find an extra activity on the electromagnetic spectrum and build on your knowledge with our Homework Helpers at www.brightredpublishing.co.uk

I managed to build a simple radio and I've made contact with another person – my radio communications reached a receiver. I have spoken to another human being and I have hope!

I can get through this. The world has changed but it's still my world. The Earth is providing me with the building blocks I need to rebuild. I have a whole new appreciation of science of and how I can use my scientific knowledge to make life better.

Problem-solving skills developed

I can:

- Research a given topic, sort, edit and present my findings visually
- Select information from a table to carry out a practical activity
- Make clear written observations of experimental results
- Select information from the Periodic Table
- Analyse the Periodic Table to form conclusions
- Analyse experimental results and make a valid comparison
- Draw a line graph from a table of results
- Draw a table to separate information
- Draw a bar graph from a given set of results
- Analyse results to correctly answer a question
- Process a set of results to inform a decision
- Plan and present a full scientific investigation
- Write an effective experimental aim
- Populate a table with experimental observations

 What you now know

Separating mixtures
- Filtration is a separation method that can remove insoluble substances from a liquid.
- Evaporation happens when a liquid boils. The liquid turns into a gas.
- Separation by evaporation can separate a soluble substance from the liquid.
- Condensation occurs when a gas cools down and turns back into a liquid.
- Distillation is a method that allows a mixture of liquids (of different boiling points) to be separated, using evaporation and condensation.

Solvents
- A solution is a mixture of substances whereby a solute is dissolved in a solvent.
- The solvent is the substance that dissolves the solute.
- When a substance dissolves, the particles of the substance (the solute) spread out between the particles of the liquid (the solvent).
- Adding more of the solute makes the solution more concentrated.

Periodic Table
- The Periodic Table is a chart that shows all the elements that make up the Universe around us.
- The Periodic Table gives us information about the mass of elements and the relationships between them.
- Elements in the same group of the Periodic Table have similar properties.
- An element is the simplest type of substance. An element is made up of just one kind of atom.
- Atoms are the building blocks of everything around us.
- An atom is made up of just three types of particles: protons, neutrons and electrons.
- The nucleus of an atom contains protons and neutrons. Electrons move around the outside of the nucleus.

Heat transfer

- Heat is type of energy. Temperature is a measure of how hot or cold an object is.
- When a material is heated, the atoms inside the material vibrate more as they have more energy.
- Conduction is the method by which heat moves in a solid. The vibration of particles caused by heating is passed down the length of the material.
- Convection is the method by which heat moves inside a liquid or a gas. Hot atoms rise and colder atoms fall, creating a convection current in the material.
- Infrared radiation is emitted by all warm objects. This is heat transfer by radiation.

Earth's materials

- Coal, oil and natural gas are all fossil fuels. These are materials that have formed over millions of years from ancient plant and animal remains.
- Electricity can be produced by burning a fossil fuel to create heat energy, which can be transformed into electrical energy in a power station.
- Burning fossil fuels releases carbon dioxide and can also cause other pollutants to be released into the environment.

Renewable energy

- Non-renewable sources of energy are finite (will run out). Renewable sources of energy will not run out.
- Renewable sources of energy generally produce no pollution or carbon dioxide when producing electrical energy. Biomass is an exception.
- Renewable sources of energy generally produce less electrical energy than fossil fuels or nuclear energy.
- The local environment will determine which renewable sources of energy are able to be used effectively.

Chemical cells

- A chemical cell consists of two metals placed inside an electrolyte. Charged particles move in the electrolyte between the two metals.
- A chemical cell produces an electrical voltage and current.
- The voltage produced is a measure of the energy being produced by the cell.
- An electrical current is a flow of charged particles (electrons).
- Different combinations of metals used in a cell will produce different voltages.

Circuits

- A complete circuit is an electrical path for current to travel through from one side of the cell to the other.
- A series circuit is a circuit where there is only one electrical path for the current to travel through.
- In a series circuit all the components have to share the voltage produced by the power supply. If one component breaks then the whole circuit stops working.
- A parallel circuit is a circuit where there is more than one electrical path for the current to travel through.
- In a parallel circuit the components do not have to share the supply voltage and if one component breaks the rest of the circuit will still work.

Chemical reactions

- When a chemical reaction occurs, a new substance is always formed.
- A chemical equation shows the reactants (the substances that are reacting with one another) and the products (the new substances formed in the reaction).
- Chemical reactions occur at different speeds – some can be slow while others can be very fast. This is called the rate of reaction.
- Concentration, temperature and the surface area of the reactants in a chemical reaction all affect the rate of reaction.
- A catalyst is a substance that can be used to speed up a chemical reaction.

EM radiation

- The electromagnetic spectrum is a range of radiations that all move at the speed of light.
- Each radiation on the EM spectrum carries different amount of energy depending on the wavelength of that radiation.
- Each of the radiations in the EM spectrum have different uses.
- High energy electromagnetic waves (gamma rays, X-rays, ultraviolet rays) can all harm living cells.

END-OF-CHAPTER QUESTIONS

Separating mixtures

1 Name and describe each of the simple separation techniques shown in the diagrams.
2 Give an example of a mixture that could be separated using each of the techniques in Q1.
3 What is the name given to the temperature at which a material begins to evaporate? Give an example of a material and the temperature at which it begins to evaporate.

4 a What term describes the process of cooling a gas into a liquid.
   b Where might you see this process occur in everyday life?
5 a Techniques to separate mixtures are very important industrial processes. Using the diagram on the right as a starting point, use your **researching skills** to find out how crude oil is separated into many different substances.
   b The following table lists the temperature range that the different fractions separate at. Use your **predicting skills** to fill in the missing value.

Fraction	Temperature range of separation (oC)
Petroleum gases	<40
Gasoline	40–175
Kerosine	175–250
Diesel oil	250–270
Lubricating oil	
Wax	300–370
Fuel oil	370–600
Bitumen	>600

6 A *solute* and a *solvent* are mixed together to form a solution. Describe what is meant by these terms.
7 By experimentation or using your **researching skills**, complete a table like the one below to show some common substances that are soluble in water and some that are not.

Soluble in water	Insoluble in water

8   Describe two ways in which the concentration of a
    solution can be increased.

Periodic Table

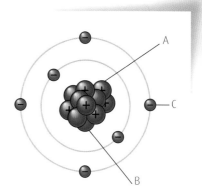

9   The Periodic Table shows all of the elements that
    we know of. What is an element?
10 Look at the Periodic Table in the on page 156.
    What information is given about each element?
11 Why did Mendeleev leave gaps in his
    Periodic Table?
12 What are the names of the subatomic particles A,
    B and C that make up the atom in the diagram?
13 Using a Periodic Table and your **researching
    skills**, make a table of three elements which are metals and three elements which
    are non-metals.

Metals	Non- Metals

14 Using your **researching skills**, find out what properties all the elements in Group 1 of
    the Periodic Table have in common.
15 The terms *heat* and *temperature* are often confused. Explain the difference between
    the two terms. Use the following in your explanation:
    - energy
    - joules
    - °C
16 Describe what happens to atoms when they are supplied with heat energy.
17 Draw a labelled diagram of heat moving by convection in a room. Show the direction
    of the movement of the air using arrows.
18 Describe the relationship between the colour of a thermatogram made using infrared
    light being emitted from an object and the temperature of the object.
19 Infrared light is emitted from all objects that radiate heat energy. Using your
    researching skills, explain how we can use infrared light to detect the location of
    people. Why is this useful?
20 Coal, oil and gas are fossil fuels. Describe how fossil fuels are formed.
21 Choose one of the three fossil fuels listed in Q20 and, using your **researching skills**,
    explain how that resource is obtained from the Earth. What impact does this fuel have
    on our society?
22 Fossil fuels can be burned to make electrical energy. What are the disadvantages of
    burning fossil fuels?
23 Fossil fuels are finite, meaning they will run out. Using your **researching skills**,
    find out how long experts think it will be before each of the fossil fuels run out or
    becomes too difficult to extract.
24 Make a table that lists four renewable energy sources and shows how they each
    produce electricity.
25 Geothermal energy is used extensively across Iceland. Find out about
    geothermal energy. Which renewable energy sources are used in Scotland?
    Explain why these are used to produce electricity, rather than solar or
    geothermal energy.

26 The production of energy from biomass is controversial. Explain the positives and negatives of this kind of renewable energy.
27 Describe how hydroelectric power stations generate electricity. Use a labelled diagram to help with your explanation.
28 List three devices that are powered by solar energy.

Chemical cells

29 Describe the components that make up a chemical cell. Draw a labelled diagram of a basic cell.
30 What is meant by an electrical current?
31 What affects the voltage produced by an electrical cell?
32 Make a table with two headings: 'Rechargeable batteries' and 'Disposable batteries'. List some common devices under these headings.
33 What piece of equipment is used to measure the voltage of a chemical cell?

Electrical circuits

34 Describe what is meant by the term *complete circuit*.
35 Draw a series circuit that contains a cell, a switch and three lamps. Ensure you use the correct circuit symbols for each component.
36 The headlamps in a car both light up when a switch is closed. If one lamp were to break, the other would still light. Draw a circuit diagram showing how this circuit could be designed.
37 What is meant by the term *open circuit*?
38 How could you control an open circuit?

Chemical reactions

39 A chemical reaction always produces a new substance. Give three examples of signs that indicate a reaction has taken place.
40 What is meant by the terms *reactant* and *product* in a chemical equation?
41 What is meant by the term *rate of reaction*?
42 Describe three ways to increase the rate of a chemical reaction.
43 Explain the role of a catalyst in a chemical reaction.

Electromagnetic radiation

44 List the seven types of electromagnetic radiation.
45 Which parts of the electromagnetic spectrum are used for communications?
46 Gamma rays, X-rays and ultraviolet radiation can all be harmful to living cells, what medical condition can these radiations cause?
47 How does a radiologist protect themselves from X-rays, when giving these to patients?
48 Explain why radio waves are particularly good for carrying messages in built-up areas.

ANSWERS FOR CLASSROOM CHALLENGES AND END-OF-CHAPTER QUESTIONS

UNIT 1: THE SCIENTIFIC METHOD

Classroom challenge, p.11

1 28

2 The Brain

3 Page 234

4 25

   a 21

   b Taste and smell

Classroom challenge, p.12

1 25.25/25

2 141.75/142

3 69.8/70

4 5

5 a 115.75 / 116 and 127.25/ 127

   b 141.5, 116.5, 113, 74.5, 49.5, 112, 95.5, 77, 157, 171, 162, 139

Classroom challenge, p.13

1 Table 1 (Metal/Bubbles), p.11 – bar graph; Table 2 (Experiment/Volume of gas (ml), p.12 – line graph; Table 3 (Pupil name/ Height), p.12 – bar graph; Table 4 (Pupil name/Test score), p.12 – bar graph; Table 5 (Time/Bubbles), p.12 – line graph; Table 6 (Year/Rainfall), p.12 – bar graph; Table 7 (Month/Rainfall), p.12 – bar graph

2 a

Type of Trash	Percentage (%)
cigarettes	40
styrofoam	19
plastic	16
paper	15
wood	3
metal	2
glass	2

cloth	1
rubber	1
other	1

b

Threat to Health	Scariness
The Higgs Boson	8
GMO food	23
Spiders in your hair	100

c

Age (Years)	Number of teens
13	220
14	280
15	340
16	420
17	600
18	540
19	700

Classroom challenge, p.14

1 19–23

2 14–16

3 18–21; 7–9

4 600

Classroom challenge, pp.15–16

1 a To investigate the effect of surface area on reaction rate

   b To investigate the effect of height on the speed of the trolley

   c To investigate the effect of reactivity of a metal on the voltage produced

2 a To investigate the effect of concentration on the speed of a reaction.

ANSWERS

b   To find out how the **air temperature** affects the **rate at which grass grows**.

c   To find out how the **number of batteries** connected to a bulb affects the **brightness** of the bulb.

d   To find out how the **speed of a trolley** rolling down a slope is affected by the **angle of the slope**.

e   To investigate if changing **the shape** of a container affects the **volume of gas** produced.

f   To investigate if **voltage** is affected by **size of metal strip**.

g   To investigate the effect of **ultraviolet light** on the **growth** of plants.

h   To find out the best **concentration of carbon dioxide** for plants to carry out **photosynthesis**.

Practise drawing scientific equipment, p.18

2 a   Beaker placed on top of a tripod above a bunsen burner

b   Test tube in a test tube rack, strip of magnesium and acid in the bottom of the test tube (labelled) with a thermometer in the test tube and held under the line labelled for acid

c   Two beakers, one pouring a liquid into the other with a glass stirring rod placed in the bottom beaker

Practice report writing, pp.21–22

Report 1: variable to keep the same: concentration and volume of the acid, size of the chalk pieces (powder and powder); possible risks: spillages, broken glassware, acid burns; ways to reduce risks: clear up spillages, ask teacher to clear broken glass and wash all areas of skin contact with plenty of water; diagram: beaker placed on balance, timer, chalk and acid labelled as lines

Report 2: variable to keep the same: distance from bunsen flame, heat (colour) of the flame; possible risks: burns, broken glassware; ways to reduce risks: ask the teacher to clear broken glass and ensure care when handling the heated equipment, if burn occurs hold affected area under cold water and seek help from the teacher; diagram: beaker placed on tripod, with bunsen underneath, timer

Practising calculations

2   Table 27: (top to bottom) 19.5, 38.5, 61, 82, 97

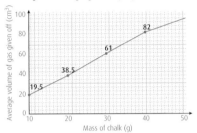

Average volume of gas given off (cm³) vs. Mass of chalk

Table 28: (top to bottom) 17.8, 15.5, 1.2, 9.4, 7.3

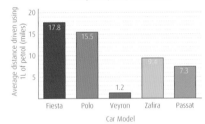

Average distance driven using 1L of petrol (miles) vs. Car Model

UNIT 2: IMPACT!

Hours, days and years, pp.39–40

1   4328.9 days

2   24.72 hours

3   Venus

4   Mercury

5   61 327.3 days

6   438 days

7   103.68 hours

8   147.6 hours

9   516 139.2 hours

10 61 320 hours

Drawing a bar graph, p.40

1   Bar graph drawn

2   Acceptable scale and unit on the *y*-axis

3 Planet names as labels on the *x*-axis

4 Accurately drawn bars for each planet according to data

Classifying planets, p.42

1 Mercury, Venus, Earth, Mars, Jupiter, Saturn, Uranus, Neptune and former planet Pluto

2 Criteria for an object to be called a planet: It orbits a star; has a (nearly) round shape; has a clear orbital path around the star

3 Pluto exists within the Oort cloud and, therefore, does not have an orbital region clear of other asteroids

Comparing planets, pp.43–44

1 Venus

2 Choose one from very high temperature on Venus; very different atmospheric composition

3 Jupiter, Saturn, Uranus, Neptune, Earth, Venus, Mars, Mercury

4 The length of a day is longer than the length of the year on Venus

5 Greenhouse effect on Venus due to dense carbon dioxide atmosphere trapping heat from the Sun

6 Bar graph should have an acceptable scale and unit on the *y*-axis and eight planet labels on the *X*-axis

7 The greater the distance the planet is from the Sun the greater the orbital period

8 An exoplanet is a planet that orbits another star (not our Sun). Planets are very small compared to their much brighter and larger parent stars. Makes them difficult to detect at vast distances

9 It is a potential 'Earth-like' planet.

10 Research should be conducted on basic facts established about the planet Kepler 186f

Calculating weight and mass, p.47

1 390 N

2 390 N

3 156 N

4 351 N

5 429 N

6 180 kg

7 405 kg

8 450 kg

9 180 kg

10 1125 kg

11 150 kg

12 450 kg

13 Jupiter

14 Mercury or Mars

15 Neptune

Solving gravity problems, pp.48–49

1 5.68 N/kg

2 1.93 N/kg

3 3.7 N/kg

4 1.49 N/kg

5 6000 km

6 1000 km

7 7000 km

8 3000 km

9 Less

10 Yes

11 Yes, the value of gravity is very small in deep space compared to near a planet or star so you would be almost weightless

Making a table of results, p.50

Distance from Earth's Surface (km)	Value of Gravity (N/kg)
500	7.33
2000	5.68
3000	4.53
4000	3.7
5000	3.08
6000	2.6
7000	2.23
8000	1.93
9000	1.69
10000	1.49

Selecting information about the Earth's surface, p.53

1 The atmosphere

2 15 °C

3 20%

4 The crust

ANSWERS

5   70%; 7/10

6   Tectonic plates

7   Iron

8   93 million miles

9   Nitrogen, oxygen, argon, carbon dioxide

10 Silicate rock

Researching global warming, p.55

1   405.51ppm

2   57F or 14°C

3   381.99ppm

4   14.73°C

5   Carbon dioxide (accept water vapour)

6   Burning fossil fuels

7

8   The gradual increase in the atmospheric temperature of the Earth, generally credited to the greenhouse effect.

9   Yes, as the greenhouse effect increases so does climate change.

10 Any relevant information, that fits within the word limit and discusses any link between carbon dioxide and climate change with evidence to back up opinion.

Classifying rocks, pp.56–57

1   Schist and gneiss are both use for building as they are both strong materials

2   Can be shaped and cut without shattering and looks smooth and shiny once polished

3   Limestone

4   Limestone as it can be powdered and is so versatile it can be used for lots of different purposes.

5   a Sedimentary – clearly made of different sized particles

    b Metamorphic – dense, has crystals within

    c Igneous -large crystals

What's the ore?, p.61

Cassiterite – Tin, heated with carbon, tin coating on steel cans

Chromite – Iron, Blast furnace, metal structures

Columbite – Niobium, dissolved, used to make very strong alloys

Hematite – Iron, Blast furnace, metal structures

Ilmenite – Titanium, dissolved, used as an alloy in aircraft/spacecraft

Magnetite – Iron, blast furnace, metal structures

Pyrolusite – manganese, chemical processing (reduction), production of steel

Time zones, p.66

1   1 am

2   4 am

3   5 pm

4   3 pm

5   4.30 pm

6   Any three countries in the same time zone, e.g. Germany, Poland and France.

7   Any two countries from the +2 GMT time zone, e.g. Ukraine and Turkey.

8   Greenwich Mean Time

9   10 am

10 1 pm

Solids, liquids and gases, p.71

1   Any three solid, liquid and gas material examples, e.g. Wood for solid, petrol for liquid, carbon dioxide for gas

2   Solid diagram should show particles in neat rows and columns with small spacings between each particle. Liquid diagram should show particles that are very close together but randomly arranged. Gas diagram should show a random arrangement of particles but spacings are much greater

3   Solids retain a shape and are resistant to compression. Liquids have no shape of their own and can flow. Gases have no shape of

their own and spread out to fill the container but can be more easily compressed

4 Solids hold their own shape and cannot be compressed due to the ordered arrangement of particles and the small spaces between each particle. Liquid have a random arrangement of particles allowing them to flow around one another. They are difficult to compress as there is very little space between the particles. Gases can be more easily compressed as there is relatively a lot of space between the particles

Marking homework, pp.72–73

1 There are three common states of matter. These states are solid, liquid and gas. (Excellent, well done for naming all 3 correctly)

2 Solids have a fixed volume and a shape that does not change. The particles that make up a solid are packed together and locked into place. Ice is the solid form of water. A solid's volume does not change, but it will take on the shape of its container. (Solids will not take on the shape of its container, everything else is correct though, well done)

3 Liquids have a fixed volume but a changeable shape. The atoms and molecules that make up a liquid are loosely held together and not locked into place. Water is a liquid. (Well done – 100% correct!)

4 The volume and shape of gases change readily. When water evaporates it becomes water vapour, which is a gas. (Well done, all your information about gases is correct!)

Food chains, p.75

1 Five examples of valid food chains using the words in the foodbank, e.g. *Leaf, Caterpillar, Bird, Fox.*

2 Producers get their energy from the Sun

3 Any three examples of local secondary consumers, e.g. *bird, hedgehog, badger*

Examining food chains and webs, pp.75–76

1 Any three food chains extracted from the food web shown, e.g. *Mango, Fruit fly, Thrust, hawk*

2 Eagle

3 Fruit fly, thrush, rat

4 Corn, flowering plant, lavenders or mangos

5 Grasshopper, butterfly, or fruit fly

6 Thrush, dragonfly, frog, rat, wolf, python and eagle

Using keys and samples, p.78

1 a *Gallimimus*

   b *Tyrannosaurus rex*

2 Use quadrats to sample the amount of grass in the field

3 Pitfall traps

Design an experiment to investigate the rate of photosynthesis, p.81

1 Any appropriate experiment, e.g. *Experimental set up the same as proving oxygen is a product of photosynthesis but having one set up in the dark and another set up in direct sunlight.*

2 Any appropriate factor, e.g. *Testing the effect of light on rate of photosynthesis*

3 Any appropriate method, e.g. *Count the bubbles of oxygen produced*

4 Any appropriate equipment, e.g. *All equipment listed in the Oxygen as a product experiment*

5 Any appropriate table (see an example below)

Time (minutes)	Number of bubbles produced

Carbon dioxide is a greenhouse gas, pp.87–88

1 Approx 400 000 years

2 Approx 400 ppm

3 180 ppm

4 USA

5 Afghanistan

6 Any three countries that have shown a decrease in 2011 compared to 2000, e.g. *USA, Australia and UK*

7 Russian Federation, China, Afghanistan, Brazil, India, Bangladesh

ANSWERS

8 Increased industrialisation, population growth, increased use of fossil fuels for energy production

9 Reduce the amount of fossil fuels burned to produce energy and instead use clean sources of energy

End-of-chapter questions, pp.93–95

1 Diagram with Sun in the centre, eight planets in orbits around the Sun in the correct order, the asteroid belt orbit in between the Mars and Jupiter, and the Oort cloud orbit outside the orbit of Neptune

2 The most sensible scale for this task is 1 cm to 1000 km

3 The new planet would have a year length between 11.86 years and 29.46 years

4 weight = mass × gravity

5 a) 8700 N
   b) 3480 N
   c) 21 750 N
   d) 9570 N

6 The greater the distance from a planet the smaller the gravitational field strength

7 A line graph with an acceptable scale and units on each axis

8 The moon's gravitational field strength would be less than all the planets listed as the moon has a much smaller mass

9 Diagram showing the core at the centre, a thick mantle layer around the core and a thin crust surface layer around the mantle

10 A day is the time it takes for a planet to rotate once on its axis. A year is the time it takes for a planet to orbit the Sun

11 The length of a day on Venus is longer than its year

12 Any acceptable example of the rock types listed, e.g.:
   a granite
   b limestone
   c marble

13 High temperature and high pressure

14 Any acceptable example of an ore, its constituent chemicals and their uses, e.g. Hematite, Iron, metal structures

15 Smelting

16 Solid diagram should show particles in neat rows and columns with small spacings between each particle. Liquid diagram should show particles that are very close together but randomly arranged. Gas diagram should show a random arrangement of particles but spacings are much greater

17 plant → butterfly → frog → eagle

   plant → butterfly → frog → snake → eagle

   plant → caterpillar → frog → eagle

   plant → caterpillar → frog → snake → eagle

   plant → caterpillar → bird → snake → eagle

   plant → caterpillar → bird → fox

   plant → bird → snake → eagle

   plant → bird → fox

   plant → squirrel → fox

   plant → bird → eagle

18 *One* from: shelter (protection from environmental hazards), water (reactions take place in water), energy (to fuel life processes)

19 Producers make their own energy from the Sun (plants)

   Primary consumer are animals that eat plants (producers) for energy

   Secondary consumers are animals that eat other animals for energy

20 Any acceptable key that allows another student to identify these plants, e.g.:

   1 Is it a single leaf?
   - *Yes, go to question 2*
   - *No go to question 5*

   2 Does it have 5 points?
   - *Yes – Leaf 4*
   - *No go to question 3*

   […]

21 carbon dioxide + water (+ sunlight) → oxygen + sugar/glucose

22 Solar energy/sunlight

23 The amount of solar energy incident on the leaves of a plant, temperature,

concentration of carbon dioxide, and availability of water. Photosynthesis is a very sensitive reaction and if any of the required factors are changed then the reaction will increase or decrease. For example if the solar energy decreases then there is not enough energy for photosynthesis to take place and the rate will decrease.

24 Nitrogen, potassium, phosphorus

25 A bar graph showing bars for nitrogen at 18, phosphorus at 26, potassium at 6

26 Advantage – aids the growth and development of plant life. Disadvantage – Chemicals are hazardous to water borne life if fertilisers pollute bodies of water

27 Suitable table showing renewables and non-renewables in the correct column heading (e.g. **non-renewable**: coal, oil, gas, nuclear; **renewable**: solar, wind, wave, hydroelectric, geothermal, biomass)

28 Carbon dioxide

29 Common advantages – 'clean' energy (no CO_2 or other pollution produced), infinite source (will never run out)

Common disadvantages – often expensive to set up, comparatively small amounts of energy produced compared to non-renewable sources

30 Your opinion should be backed up by referenced research

UNIT 3: ATHLETE!

Different people have different needs, p.80

1 2700 calories

2 1000–1200 calories

3 1600 calories

4 2500 calories

5 500 calories

6 2700 calories

7 More

8 4500 calories

9 A relevant calculation for your family members, e.g.:

1 male adult = 2700 calories

1 female adult = 2000 calories 1 infant = 1100 calories total = 5800 calories

10 She will need to eat more calories due to the combined energy demands of exercise and pregnancy

Unravel the code, pp.119–120

1 Eye colour – brown

2 Hair – dark brown

3 Height – 161–170 cm

4 Hand span – 17 cm

5 Shoe size – 4

6 Roll tongue – No

7 Freckles – None

Microbe experiment, pp.124–125

1 200 bacteria

2 800 bacteria

3 500 bacteria

4 64 000 bacteria

Antibiotic ring experiment, (demonstration) p.126

The experiment shows that bacteria will grow on an agar plate. The antibiotic ring has an antibiotic soaked into the end of each circle and that will kill the bacteria around the edge. The stronger and more effective the antibiotic the bigger the clear circle of agar because more of the bacteria is being killed.

Optimum pH, p.131

1 a 0.9
  b 0.2
  c 0.6
  d 1.1
  e 0.5

2 a 0.1
  b no change needed
  c no change needed
  d 0.3
  e no change needed

3 a 0.8
  b 0.1
  c 0.5
  d 0.9
  e 0.4

4 a 1.1

ANSWERS

b 0.3

c 0.8

d 1.3

e 0.7

5 a 1.3

b 0.6

c 1.0

d 1.5

e 0.9

6 *Campylobacter*

7 *Clostridium botulinum*

8 A bar graph with acceptable scale and labels

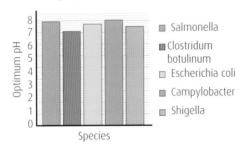

Calculations involving forces, p.136

1 10N right

2 15N right

3 0N no movement

4 20N right

5 42N right

6 567N right

7 27N left

8 40N left

9 18N left

10 0N no movement

End-of-chapter questions, pp.142–145

1

Respiratory system	Digestive system
Lungs	Stomach, small intestine, large intestine

2 a Oxygen

b Carbon dioxide

3 The heart pumps **blood** through the lungs where the blood is saturated with **oxygen**. The blood is them pumped to the rest of the body. The **cells** throughout the body use this oxygen and release **carbon dioxide** back into the blood. This blood is then pumped back to the lungs to allow the carbon dioxide to be expelled (and oxygen to enter again)

4 1 Trachea

2 Bronchi

3 Alvioli

5 A Right atrium

B Right ventricle

C Left atrium

D Left ventricle

6 Arteries carry oxygenated blood while veins carry blood saturated with carbon dioxide

7 A trigger or allergen causes the passages in the lungs to constrict, meaning less air can flow in and out

8 René Laennec invented the stethoscope in 1816 and it mean that doctors could listen to their patients' heart beat without having to lay their head on the patients' chests.

9 Diagram should be labelled correctly with the four different parts

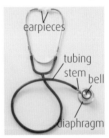

10 The open bell is used for listening to deeper low frequency sounds whereas the closed bell is for higher frequency sounds

11 As the level of activity increases the heart rate also increases

12 Pulse oximeter measures the saturation

of oxygen in the blood. This allows to doctors to make sure your heart and lungs are working well

13 Diagram with nucleus, cell membrane and cytoplasm clearly labelled

14

Cell organ	Function
Nucleus	Controls the function of the cell
Cell membrane	Controls the passage of chemicals in and out of the cell
Cytoplasm	Site of chemical reactions

15 Any other acceptable organelles found in animal cells (e.g. mitochondria produces energy)

16 DNA has instructions for the construction and function of the cell

17 Diagram with nucleus, cell wall, cell membrane, cytoplasm, vacuole and chloroplasts clearly labelled

18

Cell organ	Function
Nucleus	Controls the function of the cell
Cell wall	Provides external structural support
Cell membrane	Controls the passage of chemicals in and out of the cell
Cytoplasm	Site of chemical reactions
Vacuole	Provides internal structural support for the cell by storing liquid
Chloroplasts	Chloroplasts capture solar energy from the Sun to allow photosynthesis to take place

19 Chlorphyll

20 Slide with specimen is placed on the stage and secured with clips. Objective lenses are rotated to find the lowest power lens. Look through the eyepiece and use the focus knobs to obtain a clear image. Use the light source to ensure the specimen is illuminated from below

21 A change in magnification occurs

22 Isaac Newton was famous for discovering gravity, the use of lenses, the visible light spectrum and many other important discoveries

23 A Oesophagus

B Stomach

C Large intestine

D Small intestine

24 The small intestine is responsible for the later stages of digestion and the absorption of nutrients from digested food. The large intestine is responsible for water reabsorbtion

25 Food is swallowed and pushed down the oesophagus to the stomach. Here the food is churned in the stomach acid, producing smaller pieces that are easier to digest. The food then passes to the small intestine where the bulk of the digestive processes occur. Nutrients are removed from the food through the intestinal walls into the blood. The food then passes into the large intestine where water is removed before waste is excreted through the anus

26 Approx pH 1.5 to 3.5. The acid breaks down the food that enters the stomach and turns it into a 'sludge' this is then passed through the remainder of the digestive system. The acid also plays a part in the protection of the body by creating an inhospitable environment for harmful microbes.

27 Student's own response

28

	Recommended calories (kCal)
Adult female	2000
Adult male	2700
11–14 female	1600
11–14 male	1800

29 Additional energy is required for the baby to grow and to provide for the changes that occur in the woman's body for maintaining a safe and healthy environment for the baby

30 A Testis

B Penis

C Urethra

31 Testis

32 A Uterus

B Oviduct

C Ovary

D Vagina

ANSWERS

33 The egg is released from the ovary, where it has been since the woman's birth. The egg then travels down the oviduct towards the uterus. If a sperm cell comes in contact with the egg in the oviduct, the egg will become fertilised then implant into the uterus wall. If the egg is not fertilised during this time, the egg be flushed out of the vagina during the woman's period

34 Diagram with head and tail labelled. Sperm have tails to propel them through the woman's reproductive system to the oviduct

35 Simple microbes are genetically altered to grow insulin within them. This insulin then can be harvested from these microbes in large amounts

36 It has made insulin much more widely available and cheaper to produce, saving the lives of millions across the world. The insulin made by bacteria/yeast is a better therapy than treatment by insilin from other animals such as pigs.

37 Antibiotics kill bacteria cells

38 Alexander Fleming discovered the use of penicillin as an antibiotic in 1928 when he accidently left a petri dish of staphylococcus bacteria out of the incubator which allowed a penicillium mould spore to grow and cause the bacteria not to grow where the two were in contact.

39 Adenine (A), thymine (T), guanine (G) and cytosine (C).

40 pH below 7 are acids, pH 7 is neutral pH above 7 is alkali

41 Student's own responses

42 pH can be measured with pH paper or Universal Indicator solution

43 A force can change the direction of travel, change the speed and change the shape of an object

44 Any suitable activities and a description of the forces involved, e.g. *Carrying your school bag (pull up from the ground), writing with a pencil (push and pull the pencil around the page)*

45 Balanced forces are equal in size but opposite in direction. Unbalanced forces are not equal in size and/or opposite in directions

46 Frictional forces oppose the motion of an object. Friction is present when driving a car due to air particles hitting the car as you move (air friction) and the rubbing of moving parts against other surfaces (surface friction)

47 A Unbalanced – accelerating to right

    B Balanced forces – constant speed

    C Unbalanced forces – accelerating to the right

48 Forward force in the forwards direction. Air friction and surface friction in the opposite direction

49 Surface friction can be reduced by smoothing the moving surfaces using a lubricant like oil. Air friction can be reduced by making the shape of the object more streamlined, so that less air particles hit the object head on

50 Removing body hair to reduce surface friction and wearing a swimming cap to reduce surface friction on the head, wearing a whole body swimsuit to give a more streamlined body shape.

UNIT 4: FALLOUT!

Separation techniques poster, p.151

Filtration – used to separate different parts of a mixture by passing them through different sized gaps. Example – cleaning water by passing through cotton wool to collect large pieces of dirt and debris, and through sand to collect smaller pieces that wouldn't have been seen otherwise

Chromatography – used to separate the different colours that make up a mixture. The different parts of the mixture will get 'left behind' on the chromatography paper at different times, so that you can see all the different colours that made up the mixture. It is used to determine the makeup of different inks in forensic science.

Evaporation – heat is applied to a solution to remove the liquid (solvent). The liquid changes state to a gas and can either escape or is collected separately. The other part of the solution (solute) is left behind.

1 Any *three* of: filtration, chromatography, magnetism, evaporation or any other appropriate method

2 Filtration – dirty water (e.g. water and soil)

Chromatography – pen ink

Magnetism – metal ore when mining for iron

Evaporation – to recover salt from water

3 Heat is applied to a solution to remove the liquid (solvent). The liquid changes state to a gas and can either be left to escape or collected separately. The other part of the solution (solute) is left behind.

Using the Periodic Table, p.161

1 Noble gases

2 Group 2

3 Noble gases, Group 8

4 a 12
  b 6
  c 13
  d 30
  e 26

5 a 7
  b 20
  c 197
  d 232
  e 11

6 Fluorine

7 Lithium

8 Copper

9 Arsenic

10 Any appropriate element, e.g. *Plutonium, Radium*

Materials, properties and uses, p.168

1 Conduction is the method by which heat moves in a solid substance. When the atoms in a solid receive heat energy they vibrate. These vibrations cause neighbouring atoms to vibrate, thus passing their energy to them. This transfer of heat energy by the vibration of atoms continues throughout the solid material causing the whole object to become warmer.

2 Solids

3 Infrared radiation

4 Any appropriate answers, e.g. *Frying pan (metal for the body of the pan to allow heat to cook the food) The handle (plastic to insulate from the heat to prevent harm to person using the pan)*

Advantages and disadvantages of renewable technologies, p.176

1 Non-renewable energy is finite. It will run out. Renewable energy sources can be reused.

2 For example:

Renewable	Non-renewable
Solar	Coal
Hydroelectric	Oil
Geothermal	Natural gas
Biomass	Peat

Not limited to these answers, any other appropriate answer

3 Advantages of fossil fuels – ready for use; provide a lot of energy. Disadvantages: fossil fuels will run out; cause pollution when burned

4 Scotland uses a lot of wind power. Our weather and landscape allow us to build wind turbines to make the most of the naturally windy environment. It is used more than solar power, for example, because there is more wind energy available around our country than there are hours of sunshine.

Finding out about chemical cells, p.178

1 A chemical cell allows the movement of charged particles from one metal to another to create a voltage

2 Any appropriate answer, e.g. *Remote controls, games controllers, electronic toys*

3 A chemical cell uses an electrolyte to allow charged particles to move from one metal to another

4 Mobile phone batteries – lithium and carbon

AA batteries – zinc and carbon

ANSWERS

Chemical cell experiment, pp.178–179

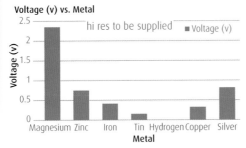

Voltage (v) vs. Metal

2   Magnesium

3   Tin

4   Any appropriate answer, e.g. *Magnesium and Silver because they have a large difference in Voltage*

5   Hydrogen – It is not a metal

Drawing circuits, p.183

1   Any appropriate diagram, e.g.:

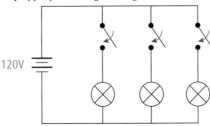

2   In a parallel circuit each of the lamps can be turned on separately, as the lamp and corresponding switch are on their own branch of the parallel circuit. As a result, if one of the lamps were to become faulty or break, the other lamps in the circuit would still switch on. Only the branch with the faulty lamp will have an open circuit.

3   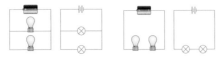

4   In a parallel circuit each component is on a different branch and receives the full voltage from the battery. Also if one branch breaks the other branches will still operate

5   Lights on a ring main

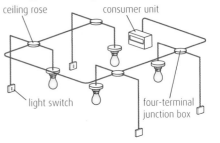

Your turn, p.191

1   a   Lithium bromide

     b   Potassium iodide

     c   Caesium fluoride

     d   Magnesium oxide

     e   Sodium chloride

     f   Calcium phosphate

     g   Calcium sulphate

2   a   Aluminium and bromine

     b   Strontium and iodine

     c   Calcium and carbon and oxygen

     d   Beryllium and phosphorus

     e   Boron and fluorine

Revising EM radiation, p.196

1   Gamma Rays, X-Rays, ultraviolet, visible light, infrared radiation, microwaves, radio waves

2   Any appropriate answers, e.g. *X-rays used to image bones inside the body to check for broken bones without needing to cut into the skin.*

3   Ultraviolet radiation – wear sun cream, don't use tanning beds, cover up – any other appropriate answer

4   Radio waves – used for radio stations and walkie talkies

     Microwaves – mobile phones, bluetooth

End-of-chapter questions, pp.200–202

1   a   Evaporation

     b   Filtration

     c   Sieving (solid filtration)

2 Recovering salt from sea water, cleaning water, removing stones from soil, or any sensible answer

3 Boiling point – water boils at 100 °C, or any other appropriate answer

4 a Condensation

 b steam from a kettle forming water drops, or any other appropriate answer

5 Oil is pumped from the seabed and moved to a petrochemical plant where it goes through a process called fractional distillation. The oil is heated and at different temperatures different parts of the oil separate and are collected. Each different part or fraction has a different use.

6 Solute – a substance that is being dissolved into a solution

 Solvent – a substance that dissolves another substance to make a solution

7 Any appropriate answers, e.g.:

Soluble in water	Insoluble in water
salt	oil
sugar	honey

8 Add more solute, or use less solvent

9 A material consisting of only one type of atom

10 Symbol and name, atomic number, atomic weight

11 He left gaps for elements that he predicted would be discovered

12 A Proton / Neutron

 B Neutron / Proton

 C Electron

13 Any appropriate answers, e.g.:

Metals	Non Metals
Calcium	Neon
Magnesium	Oxygen
Manganese	Argon

14 Highly reactive with water

15 Heat is a form of **energy**, and as such is measured in **joules** (J). Heat is often confused with temperature. Temperature is a measure of how hot or cold an object is, and it is measured in degrees Celsius (°C)

16 They begin to vibrate

17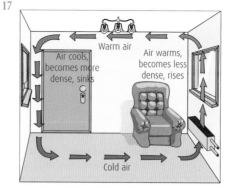

18 The hotter the object, the brighter the colour (white being the hottest/brightest)

19 Infrared thermometers are used to locate people because the human body is usually hotter than its surroundings

20 Living things died and lay on the ground where, over time, they were covered in layers of soil and rocks. Over a period of millions of years, the dead organisms decayed under all the pressure, creating heat. This turned the organic matter into coal (on land) or oil (at sea)

21 Any appropriate answer, for example:

 Oil is obtained from under the seabed by drilling down to the oil field, pumping the oil to the surface to an oil rig, storing it and transporting it to an oil refinery.

22 They are a finite resource, they will run out

23 Oil – 53 years, gas – 54 years, coal – 110 years

24 Ensure the table has appropriate headings

Renewable power source	How electricity is produced
Wind power	Wind turns a turbine, which is used to power a generator
Biomass	Waste biomass or biomass that is grown for the purpose is used to heat water. Steam turns a turbine that generates electricity
Hydroelectric	The movement of water is used to turn a turbine that generates electricity
Solar Energy	Light is captured from the sun and the photons (particles of light) knock electrons from the atoms creating a flow of electricity.

ANSWERS

25 Geothermal energy – uses heat from within the Earth for direct heating, or to generate electricity. Scotland uses mainly wind and hydro power. The weather and terrain are more suited to wind power than solar power, the government has begun to commision research into geothermal power but we are not using it as extensively as we could due to our previous priorities setting up wind power in Scotland.

26 Biomass positives – uses waste materials, considered carbon neutral; negatives – if uses trees that are not grown especially for the purpose, adds carbon dioxide to the atmosphere; can create pollution

27 Kinetic energy in moving water is used to turn a turbine. This turns a generator and makes electricity.

28 Any three suitable devices, such as *calculators, solar garden lights, space exploration transport*

29 Diagram labelled anode, cathode and electrolyte

30 A flow of electrons

31 The combination of metals used for the anode and cathode

32 A table with appropriate headings and devices listed, e.g.:

Rechargeable Batteries	Disposable batteries
Mobile phone	remote controls
Laptop	electrical toys
	games controllers

33 Voltmeter

34 A circuit that has no 'break' in it; a circuit that is not open

35

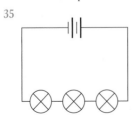

36

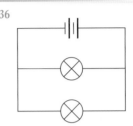

37 Open circuit – has a break in it

38 With a switch, this would allow a manual opening and completing of the circuit to give control of the flow of electricity.

39 *Three* from: temperature change, colour change, gas or precipitate formed

40 Reactant – chemicals that are reacting

Product – chemicals that have been made

41 The speed at which the reaction happens

42 *Three* from: increase surface area, concentration or pressure; add a catalyst

43 To speed up the rate of a reaction without taking part in the reaction. The catalyst can be removed and reused

44 Gamma radiation, X-ray radiation, ultraviolet radiation, visible radiation, infrared radiation, microwave radiation, radio waves

45 Radio waves and microwaves

46 They can cause changes to cell's DNA so they no longer work properly. This can lead to cancer

47 Lead vests, work behind screens

48 The size of the wave is bigger than buildings, meaning that there is no interference

GLOSSARY

Accelerate – to begin moving more quickly, to speed up

Accurate – correct, exact

Acidic substance – a chemical with a pH of less than 7

Acid rain – rainwater with dissolved pollutants giving a pH of below 7

Aim – the part of a lab report that sets out the question to be investigated or the point of the experiment, what you are trying to find out

Alkali substances – any chemical that has a pH of greater than 7

Alveoli – the tiny air sacs found in lungs

Amino acids – a chemical compound found in proteins

Antibiotic – a medicine that is designed to stop the growth of bacteria

Antiviral – a medicine that is designed to stop the replication of viruses

Anus – the end of the digestive system where waste is expelled from the body

Asteroid – a rock caught in the gravitational pull of the Sun

Asteroid belt – an area of our Solar System found between Mars and Jupiter which contains lots of asteroids

Atmosphere – a layer of gases that is held in place around a planet by the planet's gravitational pull

Atom – the basic unit of matter which consists of a nucleus (protons and neutrons) and an electrons in an electron shell

Atomic number – the number of protons found in the nucleus of an atom; the number is unique to type of atom

Average – a calculation used to determine an accurate measurement; mean average is calculated by adding the results of the experiments together and dividing by the number of repeats carried out

Axis – the imaginary line that runs through the centre of a planet from the North to South Pole; a planet rotates about its axis

Bacteria – microscopic single-celled organisms; some cause disease

Balanced forces – equal and opposite forces; an object with balanced forces will be at rest

Battery – a source of power made from two or more chemical cells

Biomass – a fuel made from previously living organisms

Blast furnace – a large container that is heated under pressure to remove iron from its ore

Bromothymol blue – a chemical that is used to make microscope slide of cells

Bronchus (plural: bronchi) – the main passageway for air to travel from the mouth and nose to the lungs

Cardiovascular system – the body system that moves blood around the body

Catalyst – a chemical that can be added to a chemical reaction to speed it up; the catalyst is not used up and can be removed at the end of the reaction

Cell membrane – the boundary of a cell that controls what substances can enter and exit

Cell – the smallest unit of life

Cell wall – the external part of a plant cell that gives it structure and protection

Chemical cell – a chemical reaction that turns chemical energy into electrical energy

Chemical reaction – a process that forms a new substance

Chloroplast – part of a plant cell that carries out photosynthesis

Climate change – the observed rise in the average temperature of the Earth's climate over time

Cobalt chloride paper – a chemically treated paper that changes colour in the presence of water

Comet – a small icy object that releases gases when it gets hot

Compound – two or more elements chemically joined together

Concentration – the amount of solute dissolved into a solvent; the strength of a solution

Conclusion – the part of a lab report that answers the question asked in the aim; it tells the reader what the results of the experiment mean

Condense – to return to liquid form from the gaseous state

Conduction – the movement of energy, usually heat or electricity, through a material

Constant (controlled) variable – a variable that could have an effect on an experiment but that is not under investigation, so must be kept the same in order to give a fair test

Contract – to get smaller

Convection – a change in temperature that is caused by the movement of a large number of molecules

Core – in the case of the Earth's core, the molten centre of the planet

Cover slip – a small, thin piece of glass that is used to cover a specimen on a microscope slide

Craters – in the case of an impact crater, a roughly circular hole on the surface of a planet or moon

Cretaceous period – the last part of the Mesozoic era; lasted approximately 79 million years

Crust – in the case of the Earth's crust, the hard outer layer of our planet

Cultivated – used for growing crops

Cytoplasm – the part of a cell where the chemical reactions take place

Data points –the results of an experiment that is plotted into a graph, or, the part of a graph that shows what average result was found

Day – a length of time on Earth, determined by the spin of the planet on its axis, taking 24 hours

Deoxygenated– with the oxygen removed

Dependant variable – the aspect of the experiment that is being measured

Diameter – a straight line passing directly through centre of a circle

Digestion – the process of breaking down food to access the nutrients and energy it contains

Digestive system – the organs involved with the process of digestion, starting with the mouth and ending at the anus

Dilution – adding solvent to make a solution weaker

Discontinuous data – information about a variable that cannot be placed on a scale

Disease – a condition that causes specific symptoms due to a change in the structure or function of a part of the whole system

Dissolved – when a solid (solute) is added into a liquid (solvent)

Distillation – the process of using different boiling points to separate a mix of liquids

DNA – deoxyribonucleic acid, a long twisted double helix that contains the code for the properties of cells

Earth – the planet we live on; third planet in the Solar System

Ecosystem – the environment where a group of interacting organisms live

Egg cell – also known as an ovum; the female reproductive cell that contains half of the genetic information to make a new human

Electricity – the movement of electrical charge

Electrolyte – a solution that can conduct electricity

Electromagnetic radiation – a form of wave energy, it takes many forms which are organised in the electromagnetic spectrum

Electromagnetic spectrum – a range of frequencies of electromagnetic radiation

Electron – a small negatively charged subatomic particle found outside the nucleus in the electron shells of an atom

Element – a substance made of only one type of atom

Embryo – the early stage of development of a baby

Energy – the potential of substance to change

Oesophagus – the tube that connects the throat to the stomach

Evaluation – the part of a lab report informing the reader about problems that were encountered and suggesting how to carry out a better investigation

Evaporation – the process of turning from a liquid to a gas

Expand – to get bigger or take up more space

Extinction event – an event that causes large parts of food webs to be killed off, causing widespread changes to ecosystems

Fair test – an experiment that has controlled variables and is easily repeated

Female reproductive system – the organs involved with reproduction in the human females

Fertilisation – the process of two nuclei fusing together to produce a zygote

Fertiliser – a natural or synthetic substance that is used to help the growth of plants

Fetus – an unborn baby

Filter – a method of removing the solid part of a solid–liquid mixture

Filtration – the process of separating solids and liquids from the same mixture

Finite resource – a fuel that will eventually run out, like coal or oil

Food chain – a representation of the transfer of energy in an ecosystem

Force – a push or pull

Fossil fuel – a substance that has taken millions of years to form and that when burned releases energy

Freeze – to change from a liquid to solid form

Friction – a force caused by surfaces rubbing together

Fungus – a micro organism that reproduces using spores, an important part of the decomposition process

Gamma rays – part of the electromagnetic spectrum, the highest energy wavelength

Genetic information – the unique code that instructs the creation and function of cells

Gravity – a pull force that acts on the surface of a planet from the core; the reason mass has weight

Greenhouse effect – the process of heating the Earth as excess carbon dioxide is added to the atmosphere, preventing heat from returning to space and causing a rise in average climatic temperature

Habitat – the environment where an organism lives

Heart – the muscle responsible for moving blood around the body; part of the circulatory system

Heat – a form of energy that causes the movement of particles and which can be transferred from one object to another

Herbicide – also known as weedkiller; a chemical that is used to kill specific types of plant life

Hydroelectric power – energy produced by using the movement of water to turn a turbine

Igneous rock – rock that is formed from the cooling of lava; also known as volcanic rock

Immune system – the way the body protects itself from microscopic invaders

Independent variable – the part of an experiment that is changed in order to determine whether there is an effect

Industrial Revolution – the transition to mechanised systems for work and transport which occurred between 1790 and 1840

Infrared radiation – a wavelength of radiation in the electromagnetic spectrum

Instructions – the part of a lab report that clearly explains the procedure, with steps in the correct order and all measurements given; usually includes a scientific diagram. These are part of the method.

Insulators – materials that do not allow the movement of heat

Insulin – a hormone produced by the body to control blood sugar level

ISBN number – International Standard Book Number; a unique identifying number issued to all published books

Large intestine – part of the digestive system that removes water from food

Lungs – organs of the respiratory system that transfer oxygen from the air to the blood and carbon dioxide from the lungs to the air

Magnified – made bigger

Male reproductive system – the organs involved with reproduction in the human male

Mantle – in the case of the Earth's mantle, the rocky layer between the outer core and the crust

Mass – the amount of matter in an object

Mass number – the combined mass of the atom's nuclear particles (protons and neutrons)

Menstruation – the process of ejecting an unfertilised egg from the female body

Mesozoic era – part of the Earth's history; a time in which life diversified, also known as the age of the reptiles

Metamorphic rock – rock that has been subjected to high temperature and pressure, causing it to become very strong

Method – part of a lab report that explains how an experiment should be carried out; includes a list of instructions, a scientific diagram and safety considerations

Microbes – microscopic organisms, including bacteria, fungi and viruses

Microscope slide – a piece of glass that has a specimen loaded on it to be examined under a microscope

Microscopic – too small to be seen without the aid of a microscope

Microwaves – a wavelength that is part of the electromagnetic spectrum

Mixture – two or more substances in the same physical space but not chemically joined together

Moons – large bodies of rock that are caught in the gravitational pull of a planet; natural satellites of planets

Mouth – the start of the digestive system; place where food enters the body so nutrients and energy can be extracted

Natural –not made by humans

Neutralisation – a chemical reaction between an acid and alkali that makes a neutral substance and a salt

Neutral substance – a chemical that has a pH of 7, most commonly water

Neutron – a subatomic particle found in the nucleus of an atom

Newton balance – a piece of equipment used to measure the force on an object

Newton, N – a unit of measurement

Nuclear explosion – an explosion caused by the very fast release of energy from a nuclear reaction

Nuclear power – electricity that has been created using the energy released by decomposing radioactive atoms; heat energy is used to create steam which turns a turbine

Nucleus – the central part of an atom which contains the protons and neutrons

Numerical results – results found during an experiment that are recorded as numbers

Nutrient – a food substance that is used by a living thing

Observations – results that are seen during a reaction, which can be recorded in writing or by visual means

Oort cloud – a group of objects, such as rocks and dust, which is thought to surround our Solar System

Orbit – the movement of an object around its point of gravity; the movement of a planet around the Sun

Ores – naturally occurring compounds that contain useful metals

Organic – natural material, not made by humans

Organism – a living thing

Organ – a group of tissues that work together in a specific way to do a job

Ovary – part of the female reproductive system where egg cells are stored

Oviduct – also known as the fallopian tube; part of the female reproductive system; tube to facilitate the movement of the egg cell from the ovary to the uterus

Oxygenated – containing oxygen

Parallel circuit – a circuit that has two or more paths for electricity to flow

Periodic Table – a method of organising the elements, which are arranged by atomic number and properties

Pesticides – chemicals that are used to kill unwanted animals, usually insects

pH – a measure of the acidity, or alkalinity of a substance

Placenta – the place where the exchange of nutrients and waste products occur

Planet – a celestial body that moves around a star

Precipitate – a liquid or solid form of water that forms from water vapour in clouds; or; the solid precipitate that sometimes forms when two solutions are added together

Precipitation – a form of weather (rain or snow)

Predator – an animal that eats other animals to survive

Presenting data – when an experiment has been carried out, the information needs to be shown in a way that is easy to understand, usually as a graph

Prey – an animal that is eaten by another animal

Primary consumer – an animal that eats producers but not other animals

Producer – a living thing, such as a plant, that can produce its own food energy

Property – characteristic of a substance

Proton – a subatomic particle found in the nucleus of an atom; the number of protons is unique to each atom

Puberty – the process by which the human body matures and becomes able to reproduce

Pulmonary artery – the artery that carries blood to the lungs for oxygenation

Radiation – electromagnetic waves

Radioactive – a property of some elements whereby they randomly lose subatomic particles and release energy

Radio wave – a wavelength in the electromagnetic spectrum

Rate of reaction – the speed at which a chemical reaction takes place

Reactive – a property of elements whereby they readily undergo chemical reactions

Reference – a record of the source of information; a way to give credit to the original author

Relevant – information that is about your topic and helps to answer your question

Reliable – a source of information, or information itself, that trustworthy and is backed up by other reputable sources

Renewable energy – sources of energy that will not run out

Reputable – respected

Research – using a variety of sources to find an answer to a question

Respiratory system – the body system responsible for taking in oxygen and removing carbon dioxide

Safety – the section of a lab report that explains any hazards and suggests how to keep risks to a minimum; part of the method

Scale – the numerical values of a graph, must always include 0 and continue in increments of a standard unit

Scientific diagram – a diagram that explains how to set up an experimental procedure; may include symbols, is drawn with a ruler and clearly labelled

Scrotum – the protective barrier surrounding the testes

Secondary consumer – an animal that eats smaller animals to survive

Sedimentary rock – rock that is formed from smaller particles that are fused together; considered 'soft' rocks

Semen – the fluid required for successful fertilisation of a female, contains sperm in a nutrient suspension

Seminal vesicle – the part of the male reproductive system that supplies seminal fluid, the nutrient suspension needed for fertilisation

Series circuit – a circuit that only has one available path for the flow of electricity

Sexual intercourse – the process of bringing a sperm cell and an egg cell together

Small intestine – part of the digestive system that extracts nutrients from food

Solar radiation – energy given out by the Sun

Solar System – an organisational system of objects orbiting a star

Solute – the substance being dissolved in a solution; the solute can be solid, liquid or gas

Solution – a substance made of a solute dissolved in a solvent

Solvent – the liquid that dissolves the solute in a solution

Specimen – an object that has been prepared for observation under a microscope

Speed – a measurement of how long it takes to move across a known distance

Sperm – the male reproductive cell; contains half of the genetic information to make a new human

Spin – in the case of a planet, the movement it makes on its axis

Star – a large ball of burning gas held together by gravity

Stethoscope – an instrument used by medical professionals to listen to the heartbeat of a patient

Stomach – part of the digestive system; where food is broken down in order for the nutrients and energy to be extracted

Streamlined – designed to reduce air friction

Subatomic particles – the smaller parts that make up an atom; protons, neutrons and electrons

Solar cell – a piece of equipment that converts solar radiation into electrical energy

Surface area – the part of a solid that is available for reactions

Synthetic – made by humans, not natural or organic

Table of results – the part of a lab report that displays the results of the experiment in a table, which should be clear and easy to read

Temperature – the average heat energy within a substance, measured with a thermometer

Testes – part of the male reproductive system, where the sperm cells are produced and stored

Tilt – the angle at which the Earth sits on its axis; the tilt causes the seasons

Tissues – a group of cells that work together and have a specific job to do

Toxin – a substance that acts as a poison to a living thing

Trachea – part of the respiratory system; connects the mouth and nose to the lungs

Ultraviolet – a wavelength of the electromagnetic spectrum

Umbilical cord – the tissue that attaches an unborn baby to its mother at the placenta during pregnancy

Unbalanced forces – unequal forces acting on an object, causing it to change speed or direction.

Universal indicator – a chemical that indicates the pH of a substance – green for neutral, red for acidic and purple for alkaline

Urethra – part of the male reproductive system, allows for the delivery of semen into the female vagina; or; part of the male and female urinary system

Uterus – part of the female reproductive system where a fertilised egg implants and grows; the lining of the uterus is shed during menstruation

Vacuole – part of a plant cell that is filled with sap and gives the cell shape

Vas deferens – part of the male reproductive system that connects the testes to the urethra

Villi – part of the digestive system; folds of tissue in the walls of the small intestine that create a larger surface area for absorption of nutrients

Virus – a microbe that requires a living cell to multiply

Visible light – wavelengths of the electromagnetic spectrum

Volcano – a hole in the crust of the planet that allows magma from the core to escape as lava

Voltage – the difference of electric potential between two points, measured in volts, V

Water cycle – the process of recycling the Earth's water through evaporation to condensation and precipitation

Water soluble – dissolves in water

Weight – the measurement of mass being acted on by gravity, usually measured in grams, g or kilograms, kg

Wind turbines – equipment that turns the movement of air into electrical energy

X-ray – a wavelength that is part of the electromagnetic spectrum

Year – a length of time identified by the complete orbit of the Earth around the Sun in 365.25 days

Yeast – a fungus used in bread making and fermentation